Cornish Geological Column

Age in million years	Era	Period		MAIN EVENTS	Earth Movements	LIFE
0		QUATERNARY		Ice Ages – Cornwall cold but not glaciated		Man, various mammals.
1.8	TERTIARY	NEOGENE	Pliocene	St Erth beds – sea level slightly higher than now.		Gasteropods
			Miocene	St Agnes sands and clays – sea level higher than now.		Conifer forest on islands.
23		PALAEOGENE	Oligocene	St Agnes candle clays.		Sequoia forest
			Eocene	Dutson basin (Launceston) sands & clays. Ball clays in Devon. Crousa & Polcrebo gravels.		Some palms.
			Palaeocene	No sediments preserved; land with deep weathering, ? silcretes.		Forest.
65	MESOZOIC	CRETACEOUS	Upper	Rising sea levels gradually submerge most of Cornwall; marine sands deposited, then some chalk.		Ammonites and belemnites in the sea. The remains of blue/green algae (coccoliths) form the chalk.
			Lower	Cornwall probably dry land, subjected to deep tropical weathering. Main opening up of the Atlantic west of Cornwall.		Forests with Dinosaurs on land.
146		JURASSIC		Cornwall probably above sea level throughout, with tropical forest and deep weathering. Atlantic ocean begins to open up as America drifts west and the continent of Pangaea breaks up.		Forests, primitive conifers and cycads. Dinosaurs
208		TRIASSIC		Land surface hot and dry – Cornwall probably a fairly well eroded mountain range in the centre of a supercontinent – Pangaea.		Sparse or no vegetation. A few dinosaurs and primitive mammals.
245	UPPER PALAEOZOIC	PERMIAN		Land surface hot and arid, sea distant. Metalliferous mineralisation at depth. Volcanicity at Kingsand, contemporary with the intrusion of the granites. Volcanoes on top of where we see granites today.	VARISCAN OROGENY	Sparse vegetation, some burrowing animals at Kingsand
				INTRUSION OF GRANITES		
290		CARBON-IFEROUS	Upper	Sands and muds eroded from mountains rising in the south fill trough across North Cornwall.		Coal Measures Vegetation King Crabs
			Lower	Deep marine conditions in N. Cornwall with radiolarian ooze & muds, some volcanicity, mountains begin to rise in the S. of Cornwall.		Goniatites Trilobites Conodonts
363		DEVONIAN	Upper	Deep water throughout Cornwall, mountains begin to rise to the south of Cornwall.		As above, plus Crinoids, a few corals and shell fish.
			Middle	Deep water throughout Cornwall, shallower in mid-Cornwall, coral reefs around Plymouth. Crustal extension forms an ocean to the south, floored by oceanic crust.		
			Lower – U	Most of Cornwall part of a fairly deep sea, submarine volcanoes around St Austell.		Primitive freshwater fish in Lower Devonian
			L	Cornwall forms part of a vast plain lying on the south side of the O.R.S. continent, with freshwater lakes.		
408	LOWER PALAEOZOIC	SILURIAN ORDOVICIAN CAMBRIAN		Represented only as fragments contained in younger rocks.		
570						

4000 – *OLDEST ROCKS IN THE WORLD – WESTERN SLAVE, CANADA*

CORNWALL'S GEOLOGY AND SCENERY

an introduction

by

Colin M. Bristow

CORNISH HILLSIDE PUBLICATIONS

St Austell, Cornwall

First published 1996 by

CORNISH HILLSIDE PUBLICATIONS

St Austell, Cornwall PL25 4DW

© C.M. Bristow 1996

Second impression with minor revisions 1999

ISBN 1 900147 00 9 paperback

ISBN 1 900147 01 7 clothbound

Design by Herrington Geoscience, Exeter, Devon EX2 9JD

Cover and illustrations by The Design Field, Truro, Cornwall TR12 2XN,
and by the author

Printed and bound by Short Run Press Ltd, Exeter, Devon EX2 7LW

Front Cover

An anticlinal fold in shales and sandstones of Carboniferous age
(310 million years old), Efford Cliff, half a mile south of Bude

The inset pictures show (*left*) quartz crystals from the
Blackpool china-clay pit near Trewoon, St Austell, and
(*right*) a fossil goniatite of Devonian age from Bedruthan Steps

IMPORTANT NOTE: Localities mentioned in this book are for the reader's information only and are not intended to indicate that they are safe places to visit. *Many geological localities are hazardous places.* Under no circumstances enter a quarry or mine without the permission of the quarry owner and/or operator, and especially **do not enter old mine workings** unless you are with an organised party under an experienced leader. Above all, use your common sense, obey the Countryside Code, and then enjoy Cornwall's magnificent geology and scenery in safety.

To begin with ....

Imagine that one summer's day you are in a boat bobbing in the waves somewhere just off the south coast of Cornwall; to the north lies the coast, with its small fishing villages and coves, crammed with pleasure-seeking humanity, whilst further inland the land rises up to the granite moorlands which form the spine of Cornwall, scattered with the remains of many centuries of mining. Southwards lies the English Channel, busy with Europe's shipping, and the north coast of Brittany lies 100 miles away across the water.

You look at the slate-grey cliffs and can perhaps make out a contorted layering showing up in places, and realise that these slaty rocks were once layers of mud which settled out on the floor of a long-vanished sea. What would the area which is now Cornwall have looked like when that mud was settling on the floor of the sea, 370 million years ago?

So, let us suppose that your boat is a time machine, and you have set the dials to 370,000,000 B.C.; what sort of scene would you find? Well, firstly you would find that the geography is completely reversed, with a mountainous land-mass or chain of islands to the south, probably with the occasional volcano steaming gently in the hot tropical sun, for we are nearly on the equator. To the north would lie unbroken sea, in places much deeper than the present English Channel, with the coastline of a major continent far away to the north, where the Bristol Channel is now. Most of the sea creatures are strange and unfamiliar; occasional rafts of odd-looking vegetation float by, washed out by rivers draining the mountainous land-mass on the southern horizon. The sea bottom is an unbroken expanse of mud with only a few living creatures such as shellfish, small solitary corals and sea lilies; but away to the east, where south Devon is today, there is a group of volcanic islets fringed by coral reefs teeming with primitive life.

Making our landfall on the southern land-mass, we find the air to be quite breathable, but there is an eerie stillness on land with only a sparse cover of primitive vegetation like nothing we have ever seen, and none of the animal or bird life which we are familiar with today. A few tiny flightless insects maybe, and perhaps the odd primitive fish-like amphibian flopping clumsily around in some of the wetter swampy areas, but that is all. Occasionally the area is shaken by earth tremors, sometimes setting off huge submarine landslides which plunge down the offshore slopes of the southern land-mass into the deeper water to the north.

How do we know all this? Well, geologists can deduce this from studying the rocks of Cornwall; and the results of these studies are contained in many scientific papers written over the last thirty years or so. The purpose of this book is try and introduce to the reader, in layman's terms, what we know about the 400 million years of geological history in Cornwall and how this has governed the way scenery of the county has been created from the rocks of the peninsula.

Author's Preface

This little volume should really be looked on as a kind of travel book, for it will hopefully assist the reader, whether a visitor to Cornwall or a local resident, in exploring the county and its geology in a way that involves not only visiting some interesting places, but also travel in time as well.

As a professional geologist, I have often attended conferences about the geology of Cornwall and been enthralled at the insights provided by many of the speakers into the kind of place it was millions of years ago. However, much of this information is denied the layman, mainly because geologists have an unfortunate habit of using technical jargon words which only a few specialists understand.

Although three books about Cornish geology have been published in past years, all are now out of date and there is very little for the interested person to read which describes the major discoveries which have been made over the last thirty years concerning Cornish geology. I have long felt that a book which tells the story of the geological history of Cornwall, in a way that the layman can comprehend, is needed. In a sense, we geologists owe this to the rest of the community, as most geological research in Cornwall has been paid for out of public funds!

The book is presented in two parts; the first gives a general introduction to the history of geological investigations in Cornwall and the concepts and terminology that are needed to understand the geological history. The second part is an account of the geological history, starting with the oldest rocks and working up to the younger rocks, with the development of the scenery emerging as a significant theme in the younger phase of Cornwall's geological history.

A glossary of technical terms has not been included: instead, please use the index, which will direct you to the place in the text where the term is explained.

I would like to thank Dr Robin Shail of Camborne School of Mines for making many useful suggestions for this book, and to Dr James Scourse for helping with the chapter on the Quaternary. An especial word of thanks also to Dr Deryck Laming of Herrington Geoscience who has taken endless trouble with the book design and layout, and made many helpful suggestions which have greatly improved the text. I would have wished individually to acknowledge all the geologists whose research has contributed to our understanding of the geology of Cornwall, but this is not possible as it would lead to a bibliography almost as long as the rest of the book! The further reading section at the end of the book does, however, provide a list of publications which should be obtainable by the layman, either by purchase, or from a public library, and which will take the reader deeper into the realms of Cornish geology. I am involved, with others, on a more academic work on the geology of Cornwall, which will be published (hopefully) by the University of Exeter Press some time in 1996. For those who want to learn more about Cornwall's geology this could well be the next step

Colin Bristow
Crinnis, 1996.

Contents

List of Figures

Dedicated to

JOSEPH HENRY COLLINS   F.G.S.

formerly of Crinnis House, St Austell

Probably the greatest Cornish geologist and an inspiration to all those
who have read his many works

Past President of the Royal Geological Society of Cornwall
co-founder of the Institution of Mining and Metallurgy
and founder of the Mineralogical Society

This volume is published in co-operation with the
Royal Geological Society of Cornwall
as it progresses to its two-hundredth year

1 The development of Cornish geology

Ask any visitors to Cornwall what is the most attractive feature of the county, and they will most likely reply that it is the scenery. The cliffs, headlands and bays of the coast, together with the estuaries and the moors, often given a human dimension by some relic of past mining activity, undoubtedly give this most south-westerly part of Britain some of the most attractive scenery in the country. The thoughtful visitor and the local person alike will suspect that behind this scenery must lie some very special and interesting geology – and they would be right.

Four hundred million years of turbulent geological history have led to the Cornwall of today; it involves volcanoes and prehistoric animals, baking hot arid deserts and equatorial tropical forests, deep seas and one of the most important mountain chains that this planet has seen. Cornwall's importance in the geological world is confirmed by the fact that Cornwall has more hard-rock geological Sites of Special Scientific Interest than any other British county.

Pioneering Cornish scientists and engineers played a leading role in the early development of geological science and mining engineering in the 19th century, at a time when Cornwall was the most important source of tin and copper in the world. The venerable Royal Geological Society of Cornwall was founded in 1814 and is the second oldest geological society in Britain. In the early pages of its *Transactions* will be found some of the papers which helped to lay the foundations for the science of geology – a science which in our own time has led us to North Sea oil.

The history of tin exploitation can be traced back to prehistoric times, with accounts of trading for tin in Cornwall being recorded in the classical Roman and Greek literature. Even today, the extractive industries continue to make a vital contribution to the economy of Cornwall.

Cornwall and the Isles of Scilly are not particularly large, compared with most English counties; but Cornwall has a very long rocky and picturesque coastline of 325 miles which affords magnificent exposures of the rocks and their structures. This has enabled geological researchers to study the geology in detail and unravel its complexities. Underground, three-dimensional exposures in the mines, and in the open pits of the china-clay industry, have also contributed an enormous and valuable body of knowledge concerning how granites were intruded, and how mineral deposits were formed. As a result of all this research activity, notably since the Second World War, Cornwall has become a showpiece for numerous advanced geological concepts and attracts many visiting parties of students and researchers from all over the world.

Cornwall as a geological unit

Whilst the deep cleft of the Tamar valley forms a clear eastern boundary to Cornwall as a county, both geographically and culturally, the same cannot be said of the geology.

Together, Cornwall and the hillier parts of Devon west of a line from Minehead to Torquay form what geologists call the **Cornubian Massif**, a convenient term for a

1

geological unit that formerly existed as a great mountain range, extending westward well beyond the Scillies. Its identity is quite different to the rest of Britain and, throughout most of the 180 million years when dinosaurs roamed the land, the Cornubian Massif formed a large offshore island separated from the rest of Britain.

The massif is now composed of folded and faulted rocks belonging to the Devonian and Carboniferous Periods of the earth's history, and was created by the Variscan mountain-building episode between 350 and 290 million years ago. Towards the end of the Carboniferous Period and in the early part of the succeeding Permian Period, molten granites were intruded into the heart of the range, accompanied by volcanicity at the surface. Heat from the cooling granites caused metals to be 'sweated' out from them and their surrounding rocks, and hot solutions containing these metals moved through cracks until they reached cooler locations where the ores of tin, copper and other metals crystallised as mineral veins.

Following the granites come the geological periods known as the Triassic, Jurassic and Cretaceous (*Figure 1, inside the front cover*), when the Cornubian Massif was an island, although there are no rocks of this age preserved onshore today in Cornwall.

Even younger rocks are present, however, of Tertiary age. Although the outcrops of these are quite small, they contain a wide range of ages and give us a useful picture of conditions prevailing when they were formed. During the Tertiary the present shape of Cornwall's scenery began to be formed, partly as a result of deep weathering of the rocks under a sub-tropical climate, and partly as a result of fault movements.

At the end of the Tertiary there was a dramatic cooling of the world's climate and the period of the ice ages began; Cornwall was not glaciated, but the world's sea levels fell, due to much of the oceans' water being locked up in ice on the land. Consequently, valleys were cut well below the present sea level by the torrential mud-laden floods in the spring thaws. In the short temperate interludes between the glaciations, the sea level rose and flooded the overdeepened valleys to produce the beautiful estuaries that now reach deep into the hinterland of Cornwall, which are such a characteristic feature of present-day scenery.

The Cornubian Massif is today the much-eroded stump of a mountain range, extending offshore out into the Atlantic, well beyond the Isles of Scilly, but millions of years of attack by ocean storms have reduced this part of the massif to a level below the waves.

Early developments in Cornish geology

Cornwall has an important and unique place in the early development of the science of geology, largely because of the former intense mining activity in the county. One of the earliest writers was Richard Carew, who published his *Survey of Cornwall* in 1602, mentioning aspects of geology and mining. William Borlase, the great Cornish antiquary, published *The Natural History of Cornwall* in 1758, in which there are many references to geology. Pryce described the mineralogy of Cornwall in a book, *Mineralogia Cornubiensis,* published in 1788; and Philip Rashleigh, who lived at Menabilly near Fowey, produced a catalogue of his extensive mineral collection in 1797 which now forms the basis for the Rashleigh Gallery in the Museum of the Royal Institution of Cornwall in Truro.

By 1805, geological knowledge had increased greatly and Humphry Davy (*Figure 2)* was able to give a series of ten public lectures at the Royal Institution in London, which included many references to the geology and mineralogy of Cornwall. Davy's lecture notes have survived and they indicate that a substantial unwritten body of practical knowledge concerning the mining geology of Cornwall must have existed at that time. In the scientific world of the day there was an intense debate between those who believed that rock formations were laid down by water (the 'Neptunists'), and those who believed heat from deep in the earth formed them (the 'Plutonists'). We should also remember that, at the end of the 18th century, the majority of people believed that marine fossils found on land were in some way associated with the biblical 'Noah's flood', the so-called 'diluvian' theory.

Figure 2 *Sir Humphry Davy, 1778-1829, inventor of the Davy lamp and involved in the founding of both the Geological Society of London (1807) and the Royal Geological Society of Cornwall (1814).*

It was into this ferment of debate about the origin of rocks that the Royal Geological Society of Cornwall (RGSC) was born. The oldest geological society in the world is the Geological Society of London, founded in 1807, and Sir Humphry Davy was one its founders; but only seven years later, on 11th February 1814 in Penzance, the inaugural meeting of the Royal Geological Society of Cornwall took place, making it the second oldest geological society in the Britain, perhaps even in the world. Davies Gilbert was the first President, a post he held until his death in 1839, a period during which he was also President of the Royal Society. Sir Humphry Davy and Lord de Dunstanville, and other leading members of the scientific establishment of the day, were also associated with the inception of the RGSC; the latter, through his friendship with the Prince Regent, enabled it to become 'Royal' by patronage.

Following the inception of the RGSC, there was a considerable outpouring of papers in its *Transactions*, with some of the most notable papers being by W.J. Henwood, published during the period 1827 to 1874. These are an invaluable source of first-hand information on the mines and mining geology of that period. Charles Peach contributed many pioneering papers on the fossils of Cornwall; he was introduced to geology by finding fossils at Gorran Haven, where he lived for a short time during the early part of the century and was employed as a revenue officer.

In 1839, Sir Henry de la Beche, the first Director of the 'Ordnance Geological Survey', published the first memoir by the organisation which was later to become the British Geological Survey, entitled *Report on the Geology of Cornwall, Devon and West Somerset*. This massive work of over 600 pages is packed with much shrewd observation of the geology and the mining scene (*Figure 3*).

Later in the century Joseph Collins, who was founder of the Mineralogical Society and one of the founders of the Institution of Mining and Metallurgy, contributed brilliant and detailed accounts of the mining scene in its heyday. Collins' work culminated in his book *Observations on the West of England Mining Region* (1912).

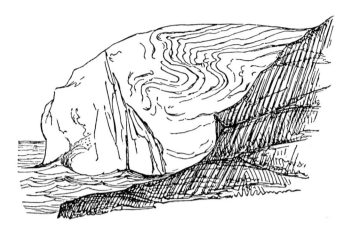

Figure 3 *Geological sketch by Sir Henry de la Beche drawn in 1839, showing High Cove, Trenance, near Mawgan Porth, illustrating the 'contortions of the arenaceous beds' (the Staddon Grit Formation of Lower Devonian age).*

Brenton Symons published the first book on the *Geology of Cornwall* in 1884, which provided a useful account of the mining geology, although the interpretation of the ages of the sedimentary rocks in west Cornwall was still in its infancy.

The Geological Survey returned to the area towards the end of the 19th century, with geological surveyors such as Hill, MacAlister, Flett and Ussher mapping Cornwall on the six-inch scale, resulting in maps with accompanying memoirs which described in detail the geology of each of the 12 sheets at the one-inch scale that cover Cornwall. Geologists still rely on the careful and painstaking observations made by these surveyors, and a number of the geological maps currently published by the British Geological Survey date from this period (*see Figure 4*).

The modern era of geological research

The spate of publications in the two decades spanning the turn of the century seemed to exhaust the available geological topics in Cornwall for researchers equipped with the knowledge and concepts of that time, and only a few further papers of significance appeared until after the Second World War. In 1930 E.H. Davison published his *Handbook of Cornish Geology*, although this was still largely a reiteration of the results of research from the turn of the century. Davison was one of the first writers to realise the significance of what he called 'The Porthtowan-Veryan line', with the geology to the southwest of this line being markedly different to that to the north and east of it; this foreshadowed the modern realisation that what we now call the Start-Perranporth Line is of fundamental importance in interpreting Cornish geology.

An early pioneer of the modern era of Cornish geology was E.M.L. (Lind) Hendriks, who found the fossil plant *Dadoxylon* in rocks along the Roseland coastline, thus showing that most of the rocks of west Cornwall, hitherto thought to be Lower Palaeozoic, were around 100 million years younger and of similar age to many of the sedimentary rocks in the rest of Cornwall. She also introduced the idea that the Lizard complex had been thrust into place during an early phase of the Variscan mountain-building episode (orogeny). Her 1937 paper was astonishingly perceptive, with many important modern concepts being foreshadowed in it.

After the Second World War researchers began to study Cornwall seriously again,

Geological Maps of Cornwall

All at 1:50,000 except sheet 322
which is at 1 inch = 1 mile.

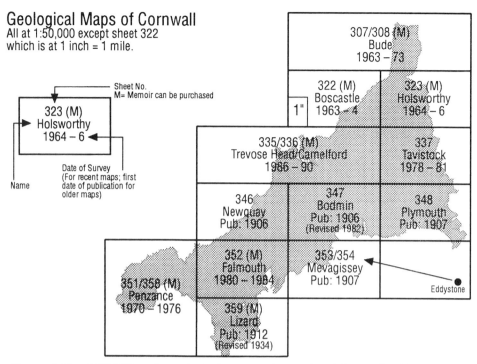

Figure 4 The 1:50,000-scale geological maps and memoirs of Cornwall published by the British Geological Survey.

this time equipped with more advanced structural concepts and methods of age determination. This enabled real progress to be made in understanding Cornwall's complex geological structure. Publications began to appear in the 1950s, and progress has been virtually non-stop since then.

In the field of mining geology, K.F.G. Hosking is probably the most notable, with a long list of publications on all aspects of tin mineralisation, including some notable papers on alluvial and wood tin. Workers on the granites included C.S. Exley and M. Stone, who provided a wealth of data on the chemistry and mineralogy, and M.B. Bott and colleagues, whose geophysical studies showed the subsurface form of the granites. A key event was the recognition that the granites of South-west England are high-heat-producing (HHP) granites, due to their high content of radioactive elements, which has prolonged their cooling and allowed extensive convective circulation of water to take place. Many of the key papers in this field are contained in the proceedings of a conference held in St Austell in 1985 by the Institution of Mining and Metallurgy, in association with the Royal Geological Society of Cornwall. Recent work in the United States and Canada has added a whole new dimension of dating evidence, which shows that the Cornish granites were separately generated and intruded over a 30 million year

Figure 5 (overleaf) Geological map of Cornwall showing the different types and ages of rocks found in the county, together with the main faults and structural units. Partly based on the 1:250,000-scale British Geological Survey maps covering Cornwall (reproduced by permission of the Director, British Geological Survey; NERC copyright reserved).

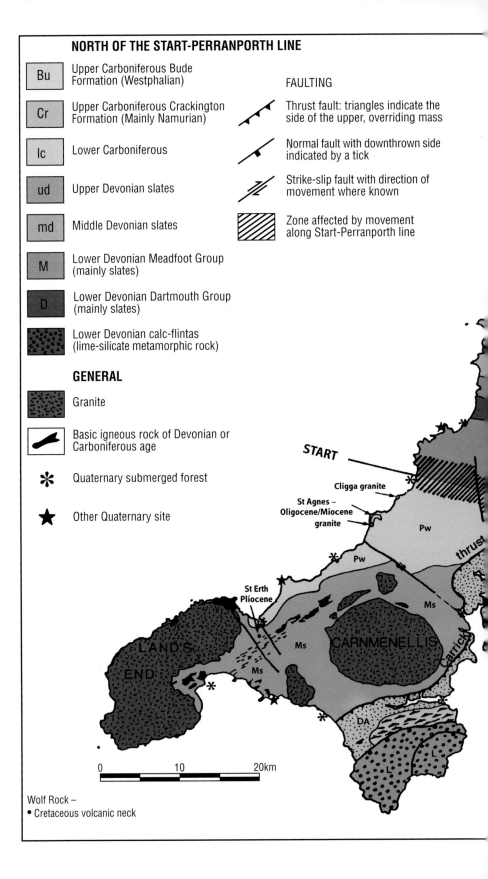

NORTH OF THE START-PERRANPORTH LINE

Bu	Upper Carboniferous Bude Formation (Westphalian)
Cr	Upper Carboniferous Crackington Formation (Mainly Namurian)
lc	Lower Carboniferous
ud	Upper Devonian slates
md	Middle Devonian slates
M	Lower Devonian Meadfoot Group (mainly slates)
D	Lower Devonian Dartmouth Group (mainly slates)
	Lower Devonian calc-flintas (lime-silicate metamorphic rock)

GENERAL

Granite

Basic igneous rock of Devonian or Carboniferous age

✳ Quaternary submerged forest

★ Other Quaternary site

FAULTING

Thrust fault: triangles indicate the side of the upper, overriding mass

Normal fault with downthrown side indicated by a tick

Strike-slip fault with direction of movement where known

Zone affected by movement along Start-Perranporth line

START

Cligga granite

St Agnes – Oligocene/Miocene granite

Pw

thrust

Pw

St Erth Pliocene

Ms

LAND'S END

Ms

CARNMENELLIS

Ms

Carrick

DA

L

0   10   20km

Wolf Rock –
• Cretaceous volcanic neck

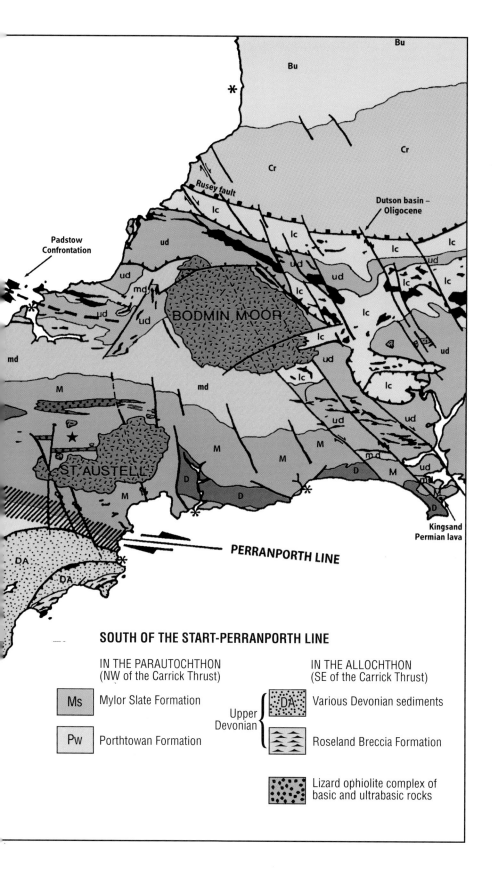

Bu

Bu

*

Cr

Rusey fault

Cr

lc

lc

Dutson basin –
Oligocene

lc

lc

Padstow
Confrontation

ud

ud

md

ud

lc

ud

lc

ud

lc

BODMIN MOOR

ud

md

ud

lc

lc

ud

md

M

md

ud

ud

M

M

M

M

D

md

ud

★

ST. AUSTELL

D

M

D

M

ud
md
M

D

M

D

Kingsand
Permian lava

DA

DA

PERRANPORTH LINE

DA

SOUTH OF THE START-PERRANPORTH LINE

IN THE PARAUTOCHTHON
(NW of the Carrick Thrust)

| Ms | Mylor Slate Formation |

Upper
Devonian

| Pw | Porthtowan Formation |

IN THE ALLOCHTHON
(SE of the Carrick Thrust)

| DA | Various Devonian sediments |

| | Roseland Breccia Formation |

| | Lizard ophiolite complex of basic and ultrabasic rocks |

Figure 6 The premises of the Royal Geological Society of Cornwall in Alverton Street, Penzance, which contain the Cornwall Geological Museum, reopened to the public in 1996.

period spanning the Carboniferous-Permian boundary (*see inside the front cover*).

There has been much interest in the minerals of South-west England, both at professional and amateur levels. The re-awakening of interest in Cornwall's mineralogical heritage is also reflected in the activities of the regional group of the Russell Society, and the re-publication in facsimile form of three of Collins' classic works, including his *Handbook to the Mineralogy of Cornwall and Devon*, first published in 1871, and his *Hensbarrow Granite District* first published in 1878. The key modern publications in this field are Embrey and Symes' *Minerals of Cornwall and Devon* (1987) and Golley and Williams' *Cornish Mineral Reference Manual* (1995).

The 150th Anniversary Volume of the Royal Geological Society of Cornwall was published in 1964, but in recent years the Society faced a crisis due to the structural deterioration of its large museum premises in Penzance (*Figure 6*). The efforts of a small band of dedicated members of the Society, supported by various grants, has seen a transformation of the building, such that it is probably now in a better condition structurally than at any time since it was completed in 1867. This building, together with displays covering all aspects of Cornish geology, was reopened to the general public in 1996.

In recent years there has been a proliferation of societies and other organisations dedicated to an interest in geology, mineralogy and mining heritage. One of the more notable is the Ussher Society, which was formed in 1962 with the sole purpose of organising an annual conference at which all those actively engaged in geological research in South-west England could meet and read papers. In 1991 the Cornwall RIGS (Regionally Important Geological/Geomorphological Sites) Group was set up, which is concerned with the conservation of geological and geomorphological sites.

The British Geological Survey has also once again been mapping the rocks of Cornwall (*Figure 4*), with re-mapped sheets available for Falmouth (352) and Land's End (351/358) in the west, and for Bude (307/308), Boscastle (322) and Holsworthy (323) in the east.

Re-mapping of the Trevose Head/Camelford (335/336) and Tavistock (337) sheets has recently been completed by teams from the University of Exeter and published. Currently, re-mapping by the Geological Survey of the Plymouth sheet (348) is in progress, which will only leave Newquay (346), Bodmin (347), Mevagissey (353) and the Lizard (359) to be dealt with to complete the task.

2 *Some useful concepts*

Geological time

Geologists have subdivided geological time into periods and given them names. It is rather like historians using a term like 'the Dark Ages', as a shorthand for around 1500 years ago, with the difference that geologists are always dealing with immense periods of time, measured in millions of years. A geological time scale covering the 400 million years of Cornwall's geological history is set out in *Figure 1 (inside front cover)*.

Geological time scales always show the oldest rocks at the bottom and the youngest at the top, for the good reason that, when layers of sediment are formed, the oldest are deposited first and the youngest lie above. In Cornwall, at times, nature plays tricks and huge folds have sometimes caused large tracts of rock to be turned upside down.

The time scale shows the names which geologists give worldwide to the periods on the left hand side; in Cornwall, the Devonian and the Carboniferous are the most significant. The Devonian Period was named in 1839 by Sedgwick and Murchison after the marine strata which they had seen in Devon and Cornwall. The Carboniferous is so-named because it contains much carbon in the form of coal, as well as limestones composed of calcium *carbon*ate.

Folds and faults

Let us now look at the way Cornwall's rocks have been bent and fractured. Most of the deformation occurred in the Variscan Orogeny (mountain-building episode) at the end of the Carboniferous, although there is evidence that some of the faults moved again later on, in the Mesozoic and Tertiary.

Folds If you place a tablecloth on a polished table and then push it from both ends, a crumpled zone will develop in the compressed area in between. In much the same way, layers of sediment can be folded by gradually being crumpled under compression.

Diagrams of folds are shown in *Figure 7* and photographs in *Figure 8*. If the fold is a downward sag, as in *Figure 7a*, it is called a **syncline**; the opposite is called an **anticline** (*Figure 7b*). Weak deformation, as is often found affecting young rocks, results in gentle or open folding (*Figure 7a* and *7b*); more powerful compression results in tight folding with steep fold limbs (*Figures 7c, 7d, 8a* and *8b*). A fold may be upright (*Figures 7a, 7b, 7c, 7d, 8a* and *8c*) or inclined (*Figures 7e, 7g* and *8b*). If both limbs are more-or-less parallel, then it is called an **isoclinal** fold (*Figure 7f, 8c* and *8d*) and it is said to be **recumbent** if it is lying on its side (*Figures 7h* and *8d*). Recumbent isoclinal folding is common in Cornwall. The **axial plane** bisects the angle between the two limbs of the fold (see *Figure 7e* and *7f*). Where you are not sure which way up the fold is, as is often the case in Cornwall, then it is safer to call it an **antiform** or a **synform**.

Folds can be of all sizes, from many kilometres across down to microscopic folds which can only be seen with a magnifying glass. In many areas the early folds have been re-folded by later folds of a different orientation (*polyphase deformation*), thereby producing very complex shapes.

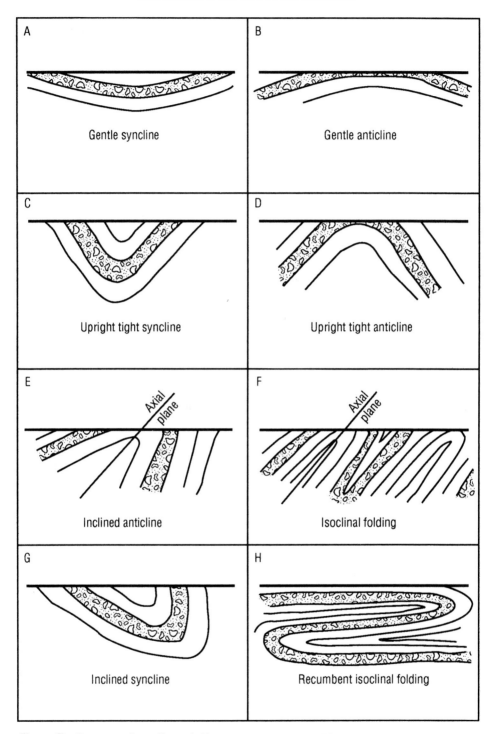

Figure 7 *Cross-sections through the commoner types of fold to be found in sediment-ary rocks in Cornwall (see text for details).*

Figure 8   Typical folds in Cornwall

a   Steep anticline in cliffs near Efford Beacon, south of Bude, involving alternating turbidite sandstones and shales of Late Carboniferous age.

b   Steep syncline in cliffs near Efford Beacon.   This syncline is particularly interesting because it is disharmonic – the thinly bedded sandstones and shales show a sharp angular fold, whereas the more competent massive sandstone in the core of the fold has bent with a gentler curve.

c   Vertical isoclinal fold in Devonian rocks at Botallack.   This fold is within the metamorphic aureole of the Land's End granite. The yellow notebook shows the scale.

d   Recumbent isoclinal fold in Devonian slates at Godrevy Point, near Hayle.

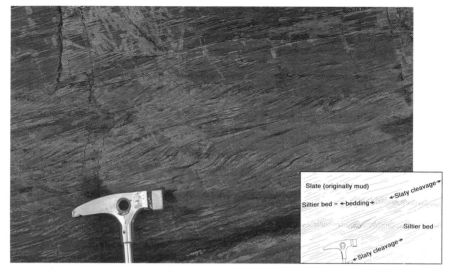

Figure 9 *Slaty cleavage and bedding in slates of Lower Devonian age at Fishing Point, near Par. Near-horizontal sedimentary strata (such as the pale silt layer just above the hammer head) are cut by numerous steeply inclined cleavage planes which formed at right angles to mountain-building compression. Note how the cleavage angle changes as it passes through the silty layer, rather as light is refracted as it passes through glass.*

Slaty cleavage often accompanies folding, for the compression that produced the folding will often cause the minerals in the rock, especially the platy minerals such as mica, to recrystallise perpendicular to the compression and so give the rock a preferred direction of splitting or cleavage. When the rock has a strong cleavage it can be split into thin sheets or slates. Beginners in geology often find it difficult to distinguish slaty cleavage from bedding (*Figure 9*). The best way to identify the original bedding is to look for the 'beds' of different types of sediment in the slate, such as sandstone, silt-stone or limestone: these are usually visible as colour differences and will often wave around in folds, whilst the slaty cleavage is indicated by close parallel lines which cut across the bedding. Slaty cleavage commonly changes its angle as it passes from one lithology to another, such as from a slate to a sandstone (*Figure 9*).

Although most sediments which started off as muds have been converted into what must technically be called slate, only a tiny proportion is capable of being used as slates on a roof, mainly because later folding has deformed the original slate, often by small angular folds known as 'kink bands', or because of joints and minor fractures.

Faults Folding is a slow process which involves the gradual deformation of the rocks by plastic deformation. However, very often the strength of the rocks is exceeded by the forces of deformation and they rupture to produce faults. Just as with folds, faults can be of any size, from microscopic to faults which run for hundreds of kilometres, like the San Andreas fault in California. In *Figure 5* most of the major faults in Cornwall are marked, and *Figure 10* shows diagrams of the main types of fault.

The simplest kind of fault is produced by *extension*, which causes one set of beds to drop down in relation to another; this is known as a **normal fault** (*Figures 10a, 11a* *and b*).   Whilst normal faults are characteristic of large parts of Britain, such as the coalfields, they are less common in Cornwall.   Alongside a fault plane, beds may be bent by the movement, causing **drag folding,** which can clearly be seen in the normal fault near Launceston (*Figure 11a*).   Drag folding can be a useful indicator of the sense of movement on a fault, and hence what type of fault is involved.   Low-angle normal faulting often accompanies extension caused by stretching of the crust (*Figure 11b*).

Another indicator of the direction of movement on a fault is the series of scratches produced on the walls on either side of the fault as they ground past one another; these are known as **slickensides**.   Generally, these only indicate the last phase of movement.

Compression can produce a range of different types of fault.   The simplest is the **reverse fault**, which is rather like a normal fault, except that the movement is in the opposite direction (*Figure 10b*).

Reverse faults are not all that common in Cornwall, but **thrust faults** are (*Figures 10c, 11c* and *11d*).   These involve one mass of rock being driven over another, usually by compression, although gravity can sometimes cause similar effects, producing a structure which looks in the field very much like a thrust fault (*Figure 11d*).   Often the lower limb of an isoclinal fold (*Figure 7h*) will develop into a thrust fault.   A small thrust fault is shown in *Figure 11c*, and a larger sub-horizontal one in *Figure 11d*. **Nappe** is a term used to describe a unit of rocks which has been driven over the underlying rocks by a thrust fault.

Yet another type of fault is produced by a kind of sliding action, with the two sides moving horizontally past one another (*Figure 10d*).   This is known as a **strike-slip fault**, sometimes referred to as a tear or wrench fault; the infamous San Andreas fault, which has given rise to so many earthquakes in California, is one of these.   Again, these are very characteristic of Cornish geology, and were familiar to the old miners, who frequently encountered them underground.   If we stand on one side of the fault and look across it (as in *Figure 10d*), and we see the other side has moved to the right, it is called a *dextral* strike-slip fault; if it had moved to the left it would be called *sinistral*, the words coming from the Latin for right and left.   Most of the strike-slip faults throughout South-west England are dextral, which tells us something about the stress regimes which caused the faulting.   These faults were referred to by miners as 'cross-courses' or 'fluccans', and the amount of displacement was known as 'the heave'.   The more important strike-slip faults probably have a long history and may reflect ancient lines of weakness that existed before the granites were intruded – some even date back to before the earliest sediments were deposited.

One of the most enigmatic features of Cornish geology is the Start-Perranporth Line (SPL) which crosses the county from Holywell Bay to Pentewan (*Figure 5*); this may be an example of an ancient pre-Devonian fault line, which was reactivated in Devonian times with a dextral strike-slip movement (see Chapter 7).

Igneous rocks – granites, volcanoes and so on

All igneous rocks were at one time hot enough to be molten.   The most characteristic igneous rock in Cornwall is **granite** (*Figure 12*), and the granite masses were intruded over a period of 30 million years spanning the Carboniferous-Permian boundary, immediately following the Variscan Orogeny.   Igneous rocks have built-in clocks, since their age can be determined by measuring the proportions of radioactive isotopes, which change at a known rate from one isotope to another.   The Cornish granites have

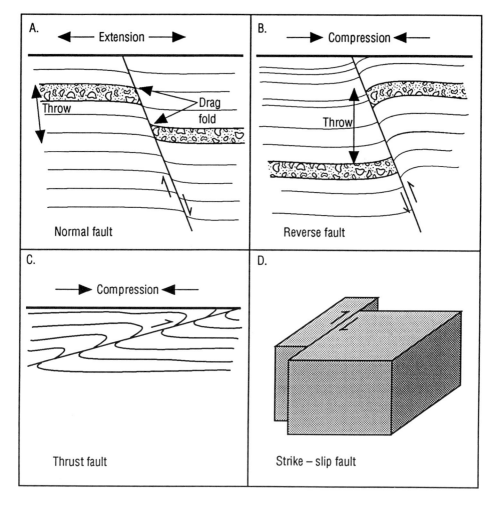

Figure 10 *Cross-sections through the commoner types of fault to be found in Cornwall (see text for details).*

Figure 11 (opposite) Typical faults in Cornwall

(The fault plane in each picture has been emphasised by a thick black line)

a   *A normal fault in Carboniferous siliceous slates at Greystone Quarry, near Launceston. Drag folding in the slates can be seen on both the upthrown (footwall, on the right) and downthrown (hanging wall, on the left) sides of the fault.*

b   *Normal faults affecting Devonian turbidite sandstones and slates at Trevaunance Cove, St Agnes. These are low-angle faults caused by extension.*

c   *A thrust fault in sandstones and slates of the Gramscatho Group at Jangye-ryn (1.5 miles NW of Mullion). An overfold associated with the development of the thrust fault can be seen above the thrust plane, indicating that the upper overriding mass moved towards the left (photograph: R.K. Shail).*

a

b

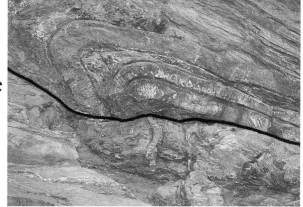

c

d

d The Greystone 'thrust' fault in
Greystone Quarry, near Launceston. The upper one-third of
the picture is Upper Devonian
slate, which has slid over the
younger Lower Carboniferous
dolerite which forms the lower
two-thirds of the picture.
The irregular nature of the
face causes the fault plane
to appear jagged, although it
is a planar feature, dipping
away from the viewer.
Although called a 'thrust' fault
in the geological literature, this
slide plane may represent the
sole of a giant gravity-driven
sheet of sediment which
slipped off the rising area to
the south and slid down into
the deep- water basin that
existed in the Launceston
area in late Early
Carboniferous times.

15

abnormally high contents of the radioactive elements uranium and thorium, and these not only release radioactivity, but also heat, just as in an atomic reactor. These high-heat-production (HHP) granites are therefore warmer than the surrounding rocks and in some areas the geothermal gradient is so high that the granite is probably approaching 100°C around 2 km below the surface. This is why the UK Geothermal Programme has been carried out by drilling boreholes 2.5 km deep from a granite quarry at Rosemanowes, near Penryn.

When uranium (^{238}U) radioactively decays to lead (^{206}Pb), it passes through eight intermediate decay stages, each involving a different radioactive isotope. One of these is an isotope of radon, a gas, which in turn decays to two solid isotopes, also themselves radioactive, known to scientists as the 'daughters of radon'. It is these detestable daughters which cause the radon problem in some Cornish houses, because the radon gas is continuously changing into fine solid radioactive particles which get trapped in the moist lining of our lungs and so increase the risk of cancer.

The larger masses of granite cooled very slowly, so enabling large crystals to grow and produce a coarse-grained granite. Granite has a high silica (SiO_2) content, traditionally referred to as an *'acidic'* igneous rock because it was visualised as containing a high content of (insoluble) silicic acid. Although it is hard compared with most rocks, it is, in fact, slightly lighter in density, so it tends to rise in relation to the slightly denser rocks around it. It is the buoyancy of the granite which keeps the Cornish peninsula above sea level, so we can truthfully say that Cornwall is a peninsula of hardened mud held up by a spine of granite!

After the granite had been intruded there was very often a final squirt of granitic magma up vertical cracks, which cooled quickly to become fine-grained **elvan** 'dykes' (*Figures 12* and *14*), often seen cutting the granite and the Devonian sediments. Fine-grained acidic lavas of similar composition to granite are called rhyolites.

The heat from the molten granite had the effect of 'baking' the Devonian slates and volcanics into which they were intruded, thus producing what is known as a **metamorphic aureole** around each granite (*Figure 12c*), with new minerals such as cordierite, garnet and chiastolite generated as a result. These metamorphic aureole rocks are very hard and resist erosion; they are superbly displayed along the coast from St Ives to Cape Cornwall.

Greenstones are what are called *'basic'* rocks, because they have less silica than granites and more iron and magnesium, making them denser. The iron and magnesium form *ferromagnesian* minerals, which are usually dark green, hence the general term for these rocks. Greenstones often form small or medium sized intrusions, such as a **dyke** or **sill** (see *Figure 12a,b*) which, because of their smaller size, cool more quickly than granites and hence their crystals are medium sized. This type of intrusive rock is known as a **dolerite** though the older geological accounts often referred to it as 'diabase'. Good examples are Black Head near St Austell (*Figure 27*) and Cataclews Point, near Harlyn Bay. Some basic intrusions may have formed a magma chamber beneath a volcano (*Figure 12d*). **Gabbro** is a coarse-grained basic igneous rock with a crystal size similar to granite, well seen at Coverack in the Lizard and Cudden Point in Mount's Bay.

Figure 12 (opposite) Cross-sections to show the commoner forms of igneous body to be found in Cornwall (see text for details).

16

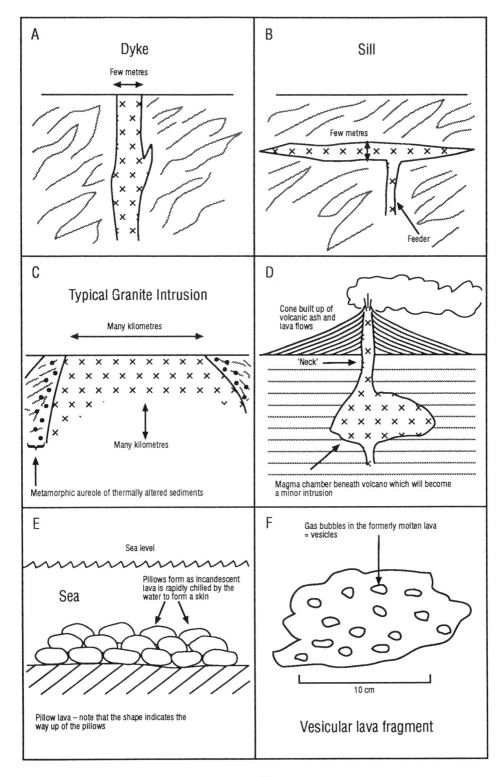

A Dyke

Few metres

B Sill

Few metres

Feeder

C Typical Granite Intrusion

Many kilometres

Many kilometres

Metamorphic aureole of thermally altered sediments

D

Cone built up of volcanic ash and lava flows

'Neck'

Magma chamber beneath volcano which will become a minor intrusion

E

Sea level

Sea

Pillows form as incandescent lava is rapidly chilled by the water to form a skin

Pillow lava – note that the shape indicates the way up of the pillows

F

Gas bubbles in the formerly molten lava = vesicles

10 cm

Vesicular lava fragment

Figure 13   *The Cheesewring on Bodmin Moor is a typical tor feature of Cornwall's granite moorlands. Long periods of weathering have produced the fantastic shapes of these granite tors.*

As magma nears the surface, the pressure is reduced and gas dissolved in the magma is liberated to form vesicles (*Figure 12f*). Most basic lavas such as basalts are vesicular although, at great depths in the sea, the pressure can be sufficiently great to inhibit vesicle formation. Acidic (granitic) lavas are prone to explosive disintegration rather than the formation of vesicles. The eruption of Mount St Helens in the United States involved a material of acidic composition.

Most of the lavas in Devonian and Carboniferous times would have been basalts erupted under the sea, very often in the form of '**pillow**' lavas (*Figure 12e*). The

Figure 14 An elvan, a felsitic dyke at the Wheal Remfry china-clay pit, south of Indian Queens. This type of elvan has a similar composition to granite, but is much finer grained. These dykes were produced by an injection of granite magma up a sub-vertical crack which cooled quickly.

Figure 15 Devonian pillow lavas at Nare Head, Roseland. Pillow lavas are produced when a lava flow is extruded beneath the sea, each pillow representing a single squirt of magma whose exterior cooled rapidly on contact with sea water. The way the pillows are moulded on one another indicates that the sequence is lying on its side with the top on the left (also see Figure 12e).

pillows were formed by a rapid squirt of molten magma being rapidly chilled around the exterior, by which time the mass had reached the size of a large pillow. This became brittle as it cooled and it cracked under the pressure from the still-molten lava within. A further squirt of lava was ejected from the crack, and the process was repeated over and over again to produce what looks like a pile of black pillows. You can even tell which way up the pillows are, by the way they are deformed in relation to those below (*Figure 12e*). Good examples of pillow lava are seen at Nare Head (*Figure 15*), Pentire Head, Mullion Island and at Great Perhaver Point, near Gorran Haven.

The actual cone of a volcano is rarely preserved in the geological record, as it is prone to be eroded away by wind or water, or washed away by the sea. However, the pipe up which the magma feeding the volcano came is sometimes preserved; a good example is at Withnoe, Whitsand Bay, where the 'neck' of an early Permian volcano can be seen in a small quarry.

Volcanic activity also results in large quantities of scoriae and ash being thrown up into the air, or erupted directly into the sea, which then settle on the sea bottom to become part of the sedimentary sequence on the sea bed. Much material of this nature is found in the Devonian rocks of Mount's Bay (Great Hogus, near St Michael's Mount), in the Upper Devonian of the Padstow area, and the Lower Carboniferous of the Trebarwith-Tintagel area.

Types of sedimentary rocks

Sedimentary rocks can be laid down under an enormous variety of conditions, so let us look briefly at some of the more important types of sedimentary rock which can be found in Cornwall.

Clays, shales and slates were all originally laid down in water as mud. Muds are composed of clay minerals such as illite (clay mica), smectite (fullers' earth is composed of this) or kaolinite (china clay), usually with some fine quartz, iron minerals, etc. The type of clay mineral is indicative of the environment in which it formed, such as fresh or salt water. Changes in clay minerals can also take place after the sediment has been buried beneath later layers of sediment and subjected to slightly elevated pressures and temperatures. We call these changes *diagenesis*, and they are more important in mudrocks than most other sedimentary rocks; this results in a mud becoming a clay or, if the pressure is sufficient, consolidated into a shale. When subjected to considerably greater temperatures and pressures, as in a mountain-building episode, the clay or shale will turn into a well-cleaved **slate**, due to recrystallisation of the clay minerals (the start of a process known as *metamorphism*), with new mica flakes growing perpendicular to the direction of greatest compression. Most Devonian and Carboniferous mudrocks in Cornwall are well-cleaved slates (*Figure 9*). Still higher temperatures and pressures will convert the slate into a **phyllite** and then a **mica-schist**. Mica-schists are not common in Cornwall, except in parts of the Lizard Complex, but some areas of slaty rocks have been metamorphosed to the level of phyllite as, for example, locally in the Tintagel-Delabole area.

Siltstones and mudstones are basically similar to the mudrocks described above, but contain greater proportions of silty material, often in the form of quartz or mica grains.

Sands and sandstones: a loose sand can be laid down by sea water on a beach or on the sea bottom, or by fresh water in a lake, or on the flood plain of a river valley. Subsequently the sand grains can be cemented together, producing a sandstone.

Figure 16 *Sandstones of the Staddon Grit Formation of late Early Devonian age at Kingsand. These probably formed a sandy shoal in the Devonian sea.*

Sandstones are typically produced where an ancient river has formed a delta in the sea (*Figure 16* – Staddon Grits). In some situations a sand can be blown into place by the wind, as the dunes at the Towans near Hayle and at Penhale Sands have been.

Conglomerates are typical of high-energy environments such as storm beaches and rapidly flowing rivers. They are composed of large fragments of rock (clasts) set in a finer-grained matrix (*Figure 73a*). If the fragments of rock are angular, the rock is referred to as a **breccia**. They can be cemented just like sandstones. Submarine landslides can also produce conglomerates and breccias (*Figures 37* and *38*).

Limestones are composed of calcium carbonate ($CaCO_3$), which can either be a chemical precipitate in the sea, or, more commonly, be made up of sea shells. Most shells were originally composed of aragonite ($CaCO_3$), which changes in time to the more stable form calcite (also $CaCO_3$). Corals, crinoids, brachiopods and many other organisms have shells composed of $CaCO_3$, and the term '*bioclastic*' is used to describe limestones composed of broken-up shelly debris (*Figures 31* and *79*). Fine-grained limestones are often called 'micrites'. Occasionally magnesium is also present, and the mineral dolomite is formed with the formula $(Ca,Mg)CO_3$.

Turbidites are a special kind of sandstone which is quite common in Cornwall. They are typically formed in a marine environment, and the sequence of events which leads to their formation often starts with a river building an offshore delta out into the sea. As the thickness of sediments at the outer edge of the delta grows, it becomes less stable and is prone to slippage. When this occurs it tends to produce a cloud of sediment in suspension. This cloud, because of its sediment content, is denser than the surrounding sea water, and hence forms a sort of submarine avalanche which charges down-slope, often eroding away large quantities of sediment as it goes and thereby

Figure 17 An unconformity at Pendower Beach, near Veryan. The horizontal beds of sand and gravel, forming the raised beach, were deposited in a warm interval during the Ice Ages, when the sea level was several metres higher than at present. They rest on much older Devonian slates which were folded, tipped up on end and then eroded long before. The contact surface where the younger formation rests on the older is known as an unconformity.

increasing its sediment load and velocity. This **turbidity current** flows down the side of the basin until it reaches the lower gradients on the basin floor, where it begins to settle out. The coarse particles settle first and then the finer clay particles, producing a graded bed known as a **turbidite** (*Figures 39* and *54*). Because of their grading and the fact that they usually have diagnostic structures such as load or flute casts at their base (see end of Chapter 6), they are useful to geologists in determining the correct way-up of a sequence containing these rocks.

Rocks of organic origin. Bioclastic limestones, as described above, are an example of the accumulation of a sediment mainly composed of the remains of living organisms. There are many other examples. In deep water marine conditions **chert** is a common

Figure 18 Fossils from Cornwall (opposite)

a A fossil fish from the Dartmouth Group slates at Watergate Bay, a primitive jawless fish, probably freshwater (Mark Beckett)

b Trilobite, Gorran Haven, from the Ordovician rocks in the Roseland Breccia Form-ation, originally collected by Charles Peach early in the 19th century (RGSC)

c Petraia-like solitary coral from the Meadfoot Group at Polruan (RCM)

d Orthoceras-like mollusc from the Meadfoot Group, St Austell Bay, originally collected and described by Joseph Collins (RCM)

e Crinoid ossicles (the stem of a sea lily) from Devonian slates, locality unknown (RGSC)

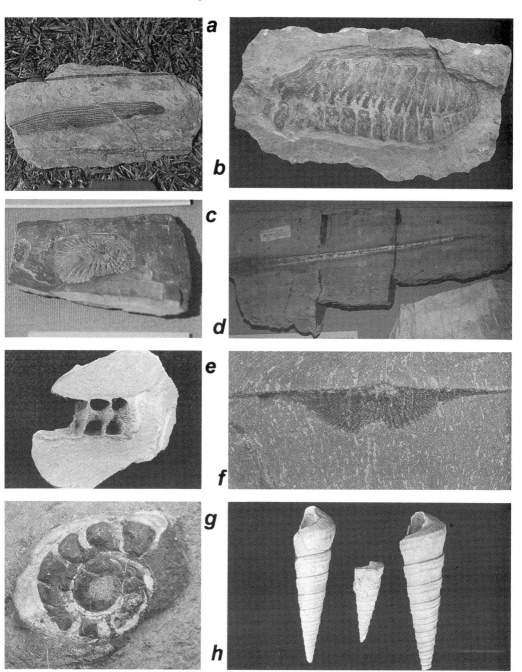

f Cyrtospirifer verneulli *('the Delabole butterfly') from Delabole – an Upper Devonian brachiopod shellfish (RGSC)*

g *Goniatite from the Middle Devonian slates at Bedruthan Steps (RGSC)*

h Turritella *gastropods from the St Erth Beds of Pliocene age (RGSC).*

RGSC = Museum of the Royal Geological Society of Cornwall; RCM = Royal Cornwall Museum.

rock type, composed of nearly pure silica (SiO_2). Examination of chert under the microscope sometimes shows the ghost-like remains of radiolaria, indicating that the chert was probably originally mainly composed of the siliceous skeletons of single-celled radiolaria (**flint** is very similar to chert but found as concretionary nodules in chalk). Occasional thin wispy seams of **coal** occur in the Devonian and Carboniferous of Cornwall, indicating the former presence of plant debris. Some Tertiary beds, as for example in the Dutson Basin north of Launceston, contain thin streaks of **lignite**, which also has had a similar origin.

Volcanic-derived sediments (volcaniclastic) are, as the name implies, derived from volcanic material which has been washed into place. Some may have been derived from volcanic ash falling directly into the sea and then settling out on the sea bottom, others may be secondary, having been derived by erosion of volcanic edifices. They are quite common in the Devonian and Lower Carboniferous of Cornwall.

Unconformities. When strata are laid down and later folded, the original bedding can become tipped up at all sorts of angles; subsequent erosion can bevel off the folded strata to produce a gently sloping surface. A later sequence of sediments may be laid down on top; this produces a boundary known as an **unconformity** (*Figure 17*). Sometimes the interval of geological time between the deposition of the older and younger sequences can be huge, as in the case of *Figure 17*, where the sediments of the Devonian Pendower Formation (below the unconformity) were laid down about 380 million years ago, and the Quaternary raised-beach sediments above the unconformity were laid down in one of the warm interludes in the ice ages, about 200,000 years ago. Another good example is seen half a mile east of Kingsand, where Permian breccias and lavas rest *unconformably* on the older Devonian Staddon Grit Formation

Fossils from Cornwall – the remains of ancient life

Fossils are the remains of plants and animals which have been preserved in the sediments, and the study of fossils is known as *palaeontology*. The soft parts of an animal are only preserved under exceptional conditions but the hard parts, such as a sea shell, a coral or the hard scales of a fish, are often fossilised – sometimes as the original hard material of the organism, or they may be replaced by another mineral.

Because of the effects of the Variscan Orogeny, the fossils found in the Devon and Carboniferous rocks of Cornwall are often distorted, fragmentary and difficult to recognise. When looking for fossils it is always advisable to search surfaces where the slaty cleavage and the bedding are more or less parallel. The spectacular fossils found in younger rocks further east in Britain are generally absent in Cornwall. Huge thicknesses of sediment can be almost devoid of recognisable fossils to the naked eye, as in the case of the Devonian rocks of west Cornwall.

As most of the Devonian and Carboniferous sediments in Devon and Cornwall were laid down under marine conditions, and most of the fossils are of marine creatures such as brachiopods (shellfish – *Figure 18f*), corals (*Figure 18c*), trilobites (an extinct form of arthropod – *Figure 18b*) and goniatites (a mollusc with a coiled shell, something like the modern nautilus – *Figure 18g*). The small discs from crinoid stems, known as 'crinoid ossicles', typically 5-10 mm in diameter, are probably the commonest fossils in Devonian sediments (*Figure 18e*). In the earliest Devonian rocks, fish fossils are common (*Figure 18a*).

Land-plant fossils are known from the Middle Devonian in south Cornwall and the

Upper Carboniferous of north Cornwall, as well as a few other locations. These plants were washed into the sea from the land and then sank to the bottom where they were fossilised.

Fossils are valuable indicators of the age of the sediments and detailed subdivision of the Devonian and Carboniferous rocks is made possible by using the various types of animal and plant fossils as they evolved through geological time. Particularly useful fossils in this respect are the goniatites and trilobites. The Devonian and Carboniferous rocks of Cornwall can be readily correlated with the beds of the same age in France, Belgium and Germany by means of these.

Collecting **macrofossils** (those visible to the naked eye) can be a time-consuming business if you want to find specimens sufficiently well preserved to be identifiable, and the places where good macrofossils can be obtained are few and far between. So, over the last thirty years, there has been a shift away from the use of macrofossils to the use of **microfossils** (fossils only visible with the aid of a microscope), and laboratory techniques have been developed to extract microfossils from rocks collected in the field.

The study of plant spores and pollen is known as *palynology*, and these are often surprisingly well preserved and are particularly useful for age determination. After years of uncertainty, the sedimentary rocks of west Cornwall have finally been dated by means of palynology.

Another particularly useful group of microfossils are the **conodonts**. These are usually obtained by dissolving limestones in dilute acetic acid, in which the phosphatic conodonts are insoluble. After further concentration, the minute comb-like and tooth-like conodonts can be recovered and identified under the microscope. For a long time the biological affinities of conodonts were unknown, but recent discoveries of conodonts with their soft parts preserved has shown that they represent the feeding apparatus of a primitive back-boned free-swimming animal. Conodonts are exceptionally useful for age determination and enable precise dating into relatively short time zones to be achieved.

The wandering continents and plate collisions

No geological account nowadays is complete without a reference to *plate tectonics*, and it is certainly helpful to understanding what went on in the Devonian and Carboniferous periods in the area we now call Cornwall.

The earth's crust under the continents is different to that under the oceans (*Figure 19*). The **continental crust** is lighter, being composed of rocks with approximately the composition of granite. Many of the younger sediments which make up continental crust are lighter still. The continents form raft-like masses floating on the surface of the layer below, which is heavier and denser, being composed of basic and ultrabasic rocks like gabbros and peridotites. Under the oceans these denser rocks form **oceanic crust**, with no lighter continental crust on top.

The surface of our planet is made up of a series of **crustal plates**, some of colossal size and some quite small. The revolutionary concept that came in with plate tectonics was the realisation that these plates are continuously moving: in some places a plate is diving below another plate and being destroyed, and in other places a new plate is being created. The continents get carried along on the surface of a plate, like the week's groceries on the conveyor belt at a supermarket checkout. Where there is a destructive margin (beside the cashier!), the continental material (the week's groceries) is too light

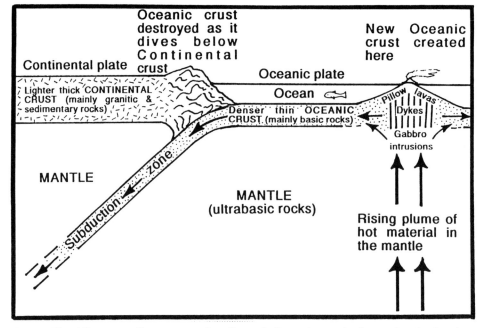

Figure 19 *Diagrammatic cross-section through the outer part of our planet, showing the crust and underlying upper part of the mantle. On the right, a rising plume of material from the mantle is causing new oceanic crust to be created at a spreading axis, and in the centre the oceanic crust is being destroyed as it descends back down into the mantle along a subduction zone (the locus of many earthquakes). The lighter, thicker and more buoyant continental crust is shown on the left.*

to be pulled down under the adjoining plate, so it piles up at the point where it is passing under that plate, just like the groceries would if the cashier did not pass them to the customer. This process is called *subduction* – see *Figure 19*.

In some cases the conveyor belts carry two continental masses towards one another and a *continental collision* occurs, which is what is happening at present where the Indian sub-continent is colliding with the southern side of Asia, raising up Tibet and the Himalayas in the process. In other cases, where there is continent on one side of the subduction zone and oceanic crust on the other side, a coastal mountain range like the Andes is formed. Where two oceanic plates collide, this usually results in a deep trench with a line of volcanic islands, known as an **island arc**, on one side. Sometimes there are sediments or a series of scraps of continental material riding on the plate (conveyor) which get scraped off as one plate passes down below another and are accreted onto the edge of a larger continental mass. The various mountain ranges that go to make up the western coast of North America are in this category; it may also have occurred in Cornwall.

So, if all this crust is being destroyed during collisions, where is the new crust to make up for it being created? In the centres of the oceans there are huge long linear ridges or **spreading axes**, usually with a great deal of volcanic and earthquake activity associated with them. These are the areas where new oceanic crust (or plate) is being created (*Figure 19*). It would seem that there are convection currents in the mantle, which rise below these ridges and then spread sideways away from the ridge. This is where the conveyor belt comes up. Most of these spreading axes are below water and only occasionally do they poke above sea level, as in Iceland or the Azores. The lavas erupted below water very often take the form of pillow lavas (*Figures 12e* and *15*). Oceanic crust therefore usually consists of a thin layer of sediments resting on basaltic pillow lavas, below which are intrusions of basic magma formed when the crust was created at the spreading axis.   The Lizard Complex is a dismembered Devonian spreading axis, in which all the components of oceanic crust can be recognised.

Sometimes a rising current in the mantle will come up under a continent and cause it to break up. The initial stages produce rift valleys and volcanicity, as we see today in East Africa and the Red Sea; later, as the sides gradually move apart, a new ocean is created. At several stages in the earth's history a 'supercontinent' comprising a high proportion of the earth's continental crust has been created, only for it to subsequently break up and re-group in a new way.

Palaeomagnetism. It is possible to deduce where a piece of continental crust was, at any period of geological time, by measuring the magnetic orientation of iron-bearing minerals in lavas or sediments. When these feebly magnetic minerals were formed from the lava by crystallisation, or by being deposited in the sediment, they became aligned to the earth's magnetic field, giving rise to a weak 'remanent' magnetism. By excluding the earth's field and measuring this remanent magnetism, the position of that plate in relation to the magnetic poles at the time the lava or sediment was formed can be determined. By making many measurements of the palaeomagnetic field over a wide range of geological ages, the track of the continents as they wandered around on the surface of the planet can be worked out. The results show that the continents have moved around far more than we used to believe possible. Most of Britain seems to have started off at a high latitude in the southern hemisphere 500 million years ago in the Cambrian Period, and then moved northwards ever since.

How plate tectonics can be applied to the Variscan Orogeny (mountain-building episode) is still highly controversial. The palaeomagnetic measurements indicate that, during the Devonian Period Cornwall lay close to the Equator, perhaps just into the southern hemisphere. During the Devonian and Carboniferous, a northward-moving plate, comprising most of what is now France, appears to have rammed into the southern edge of a mighty continent known as Laurasia which then comprised most of Northern Europe and North America (the Atlantic Ocean is a later creation). The process of collision is complicated and it looks as if the collision was oblique and, at times, the process may have even gone into reverse, so producing a north-south crustal extension.

The land-mass which existed in Devonian times at the leading edge of the French plate is known as '**Normannia**' to geologists and it plays quite a significant role in the Devonian history of Cornwall. As most of the features of a mid-oceanic spreading axis can be recognised in the Lizard, this suggests that an ocean may have existed between Brittany and Cornwall at an early stage in the Devonian Period, which is called by geologists the **Rheic Ocean,** although we know little about it or even where it was.

3 *Wealth from the ground*

Mining in Cornwall

The mineral wealth of Cornwall has been, and still is, prodigious. *Table 1* below shows the total values, at today's prices, of all the minerals that have been extracted from the Cornubian orefield.

The Cornubian orefield is by no means exhausted although nowadays china clay is the most important mineral extracted; as the table shows, the value of china clay extracted has now overtaken all the other minerals put together. Current production of china clay is just over 2.5 million tonnes a year, and in the last ten years the china-clay industry has produced more clay than in any other ten-year period in its history. China clay is now Britain's second most important mineral export, after petroleum. The main

Table 1 Mineral production from the Cornubian orefield[*] from B.C. to the present

Commodity	Total production (tonnes)	1995 unit value (£/tonne)	Total production value (1995 prices)
China clay	150,000,000	£80	£12,000m
Tin metal	1,500,000	£4,000	£6,000m
Copper metal	2,000,000	£1,800	£3,600m
China stone	5,000,000	£85	£425m
Lead metal	250,000	£375	£94m
Zinc metal	96,500	£630	£61m
Iron ore	2,000,000	£12	£24m
Silver, from lead	233	£80,000	£18m
Barytes	450,000	£40	£18m
Tungsten ore (wolfram, WO_3)	5,600	£3,000	£17m
Manganese ore	100,000	£100	£10m
Gold	1	£7.8m	£8m
Silver ore	2,000	£2,000	£4m
Arsenic ore (As_2O_3)	250,000	£15	£4m
Pyrite (FeS_2)	150,000	£12	£2m
Fluorspar (CaF_2)	10,200	£100	£1m
TOTALS	162,000,000		£22,290m

[*] The Cornubian orefield includes the whole of Cornwall and those mineralised areas associated with the Dartmoor granite. In addition to the commodities listed above, much granite and other rocks have been quarried for constructional use.

use for china clay is in paper. Small quantities of china stone, a granite with a very low content of iron-bearing dark minerals, are still produced from the St Austell granite for use in ceramics, although not as much in former years due to imports of feldspathic material from Scandinavia.

Metalliferous mining in Cornwall dates back to prehistoric times. Initially, most of the tin was won from alluvial deposits, but later underground mining took over as the principal source of the ore. However, mining of copper became more important than tin for a while in the early part of the 19th century, but collapsed in the 1860s due to cheap ore from overseas undercutting the economic viability of Cornish copper mining.

Besides tin, copper and china clay, many other metals and non-metallic ores have been produced from the Cornubian orefield as *Table 1* shows. Some, such as arsenic, no longer have any significant market, so are no longer produced.

The exceptional range of metalliferous deposits in the Cornubian orefield has led to a tremendous variety of unusual and rare minerals being present (*Figure 21*), and many mineral species are only known from this orefield. A visit to the Rashleigh Gallery at the Royal Cornwall Museum in Truro, the Camborne School of Mines Museum near Redruth or the Cornwall Geological Museum in Penzance will demonstrate how rich and varied this mineral heritage is.

Mineral lodes are often found in and around igneous intrusions, especially granites, the essential factors in their creation being heat and water. For metalliferous deposits there also has to be a source of the metals themselves, usually present at low concentrations in the granite and the surrounding sediments, and heat and water are the means to concentrate them into workable mineral veins. The water can come from the intrusion itself ('magmatic water'), or it can be water ultimately derived from rainfall which has soaked into the ground ('meteoric water'). Mineralising fluids often take the form of a salty brine laden with metals and other elements; the formation of metalliferous mineral lodes can take place when such a fluid is cooled so the metal-liferous minerals precipitate out, or it can be caused by a briny metal-bearing fluid mixing with another fluid of different composition, thereby causing a chemical reaction to take place which precipitates the mineral.

The source of the heat usually lies in the granite itself, for not only is there the residual heat which the molten granite possessed when it flowed into place, but also the heat from the radioactive elements in the granite which, in the case of the Cornish granites, was sufficient to prolong the cooling of the granite considerably, especially at the low-temperature end of the cooling curve. This heat created ideal conditions for metals like tin and copper to be leached out of the granite and the surrounding rocks. These were then carried in solution to cooler areas where the minerals could be precipitated in fractures, forming the tin and copper bearing veins exploited by generations of Cornish miners. More will be said about the Cornubian orefield in Chapter 9.

Copper mainly occurs as the brassy-looking mineral **chalcopyrite** (*Figure 20a*), an iron/copper sulphide ($CuFeS_2$), which is easily confused with pyrite (FeS_2) or 'fool's gold'. Chalcopyrite is easily broken down by weathering (*Figure 69*).

The only worthwhile ore mineral of tin is a dark-brown mineral called **cassiterite** (*Figure 20b*), which is tin oxide (SnO_2). Nowadays, tin mining in Cornwall is reduced to one large deep underground mine – South Crofty – between Redruth and Camborne.

Hard though granite is, it will slowly be weathered away, especially if the climate is warm and wet as in the present-day tropics. For much of the 270 million years since

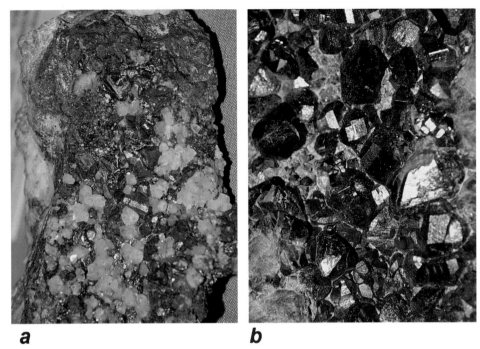

a   **b**

Figure 20   The two most important ore minerals in Cornish mining – chalcopyrite and cassiterite.

a   *Chalcopyrite (CuFeS₂, the brassy-looking mineral, with tetrahedrite), is the main copper-containing mineral found in Cornwall; copper mining was highly profitable in the first half of the 19th century. Specimen from Herodsfoot, Lanreath.*

b   *Cassiterite (SnO₂, the dark brown mineral) from the Trevaunance Mine, St Agnes. Practically all the tin recovered in Cornwall was in the form of cassiterite. Photographs courtesy of the Royal Cornwall Museum.*

Figure 21 (opposite) A variety of minerals from Cornwall

a *Haematite from the Restormel Royal Iron Mine*

b *Quartz crystals from Blackpool china-clay pit*

c *An orthoclase feldspar megacryst ("pigs eggs") from Melbur china-clay pit, near St Stephen.*

d *Twinned pyrite cubes from Greystone Quarry, near Launceston*

e *Galena from a lode in Greystone Quarry, near Launceston*

f *Natrolite (a zeolite) from Dean Quarry, near St Keverne*

g *Meta-torbernite (a secondary uranium bearing mineral) from Gunnislake Old Mine, Calstock*

h *Turquoise from Gunheath china-clay pit*

*All specimens from the author's collection, except **g** which is from the Royal Cornwall Museum.*

a

b

c

d

e

f

g

h

Figure 22 *A Cornish engine house at Botallack Mine, near St Just. This famous tin and copper mine extended under the sea. The adjacent Geevor mine only closed in 1990. The building in the photograph housed the beam engine which pumped water from the workings.*

the granites were intruded, the Cornish climate has been tropical or sub-tropical, but even under tropical conditions cassiterite will resist weathering and accumulate at or near the surface, as the rest of the minerals are weathered away. More recently, there have been the ice ages, which have caused the soft tin-bearing weathered material to be washed down into the valleys, where the heavy cassiterite was further concentrated in tin-bearing sands and gravels. These deposits of 'alluvial' or 'stream' tin were the main source of the ore until the 18th century, and nearly half of all the tin produced over the centuries from Cornwall came from tin streaming. Sometimes a small amount of gold was recovered as well.

As we look today at the engine houses and other romantic relics of Cornwall's mining past (*Figure 22*), we should not forget what they represent. Generations of

Figure 23 *Cornish miners underground in the last century. This view in Chappel's shaft at the 406 fathom level of Cook's Kitchen mine, near Pool, is nearly half a mile below surface. Photograph taken by J.C. Burrow in the 1890s (Royal Cornwall Museum).*

miners gave their short working lives to extract tin and copper ore from deep underground, working in difficult conditions, with inadequate light, often hungry and ill, dying as old men in their thirties (*Figure 23*). These men provided one of the keystones for the early economic growth of Britain – something which we are still enjoying the fruits of.

These pioneers also laid the foundations for the development of mining engineering and mining geology. Spiritually, in their short working lives, they probably were richer than people nowadays – as witnessed by the community spirit and faith which led to the building of chapels in almost every mining community in Cornwall. When the great mining crash came in the 1870s there was no welfare state to fall back on so, faced with the prospect of starvation, they emigrated overseas to wherever in the world their mining skills were in demand – South America, the United States, Australia, South Africa and many other places. A well-known old definition of a mine is a hole with a Cornishman at the bottom!

Building stones of Cornwall

Stone has been extensively used for building in Cornwall since Neolithic times, and the most famous material, of course, has been **granite**. Granite quarries have been opened in all the main granite masses and many of the standing stones and hut circles in Cornwall are formed of granite, so its use may well have a history stretching back for four thousand years or more. Early working probably involved retrieving large blocks of loose granite ('moorstone') lying on the surface and then shaping them for use; only later were quarries opened to provide stone.

Excellent-quality granite, for use as a dimension stone (dimension stone = stone which can be cut into regularly shaped blocks) is still worked in De Lank and Hanter-gantick quarries on the west side of Bodmin Moor. This coarse-grained megacrystic biotite granite (megacrysts = big crystals, biotite = dark-brown iron-bearing mica) was used in many famous lighthouses (e.g. Eddystone, Bishop Rock and Beachy Head) and bridges (e.g. Tower and Blackfriars bridges in London). A large quarry below the Cheesewring, on the southeast side of Bodmin Moor, also yielded high-quality granite which was taken for shipment at Looe via the Caradon railway.

Figure 24 Cornish building materials (overleaf)

a *Truro cathedral exterior is of Penryn granite, the interior a finer-grained granite from 'Cathedral Quarry', near Nanpean. Note the sand waste tips of the St Austell china-clay industry on the horizon behind the spire.*

b *Place, Fowey, the former residence of Joseph Treffry, the great 19th-century Cornish entrepreneur and quarry owner. The 15th-century part (on the right) is built of Pen-tewan stone and local slate; Porphyry Hall and Tower (19th century) at the rear is built of Luxulyan granite. The interior of Porphyry Hall is lined with polished slabs of luxullianite (see **d**, below) and an elvan from Tremore, near Withiel.*

c *Some superb carving in Pentewan stone on the 15th-century tower of St Austell parish church.*

d *Luxullianite, a variety of granite from Tregarden Quarry, Luxulyan. The black is tour-maline and the pink orthoclase feldspar. This striking ornamental stone was used for the Duke of Wellington's sarcophagus in St Paul's Cathedral (specimen 10 cm wide)*

a

b

c

d

Figure 24 **Cornish building materials** *(continued)*

e Polyphant stone in the War Memorial adjacent to the West Door, Truro Cathedral.

f Cataclews stone: a 15th-century font carved by an unknown sculptor known to architectural historians as 'The Master of St Endellion', St Petroc's Church, Padstow.

g Delabole slate (window-sill) and St Issey slate (wall) used in a contemporary building.

h Quaternary sandrock, 14th-century arch in St Carantocus church, Crantock. This is one of the geologically youngest building stones (150,000 years old) to be found anywhere in Britain.

High-quality biotite granite with large white megacrysts of orthoclase feldspar was formerly quarried from the Luxulyan area (Tregarden, Carbean, Colcerrow and Orchard quarries) and many famous buildings (e.g. the British Museum) and engineering structures (e.g. the old London Bridge and Plymouth Breakwater) were constructed from it. The exterior of Porphyry Hall and the Tower at Place, Fowey are of Luxulyan granite (*Figure 24b*). A striking variant of the Luxulyan granite is 'luxullianite', which is made up of coarse black tourmaline needle-like crystals and deep-pink orthoclase feldspar (*Figure 24d*).

Granite has also been extensively quarried in the south-eastern part of the Carnmenellis granite, where proximity to loading wharves in the Fal Estuary led to a substantial industry in the 19th century; there are still several active quarries, mostly now producing crushed aggregate for general constructional work. Carnsew Quarry, near Mabe, provided the stone for the exterior of Truro Cathedral (*Figure 24a*). A leaflet on the many Cornish building stones which have been incorporated into the fabric is available from the Cathedral bookstall. A derelict quarry at Lamorna Cove, on the southern side of the Land's End granite, formerly produced high-quality dimension stone from a coarse-grained biotite granite (*Figure 6*) which was used locally and exported from a small harbour in the cove.

The felsitic elvans of Cornwall (not to be confused with 'blue' elvans, see below) are among Cornwall's finest building stones. They have the same chemical composition as the granites but, because they cooled more rapidly, are of much finer grain and are often only weakly kaolinised. The most famous is **Pentewan stone**, which forms a dyke in the cliffs about a quarter of a mile northeast of Pentewan. This is one of Cornwall's few freestones (freestone = a stone which can be carved freely into intricate shapes) and has been worked from medieval times. St Austell parish church and Place, Fowey, used this stone (*Figure 24b* and *c*). It is a lovely golden-yellow colour, often with tinges of pink, and stands up to weathering surprisingly well, partly because it is not slowly dissolved away by the rainwater, as limestone is. Prolonged exposure to the weather, as can be seen at the base of St Austell church tower, leads to the surface layer of the stone developing a honeycomb texture, due to the weakly kaolinised feldspars being washed away by the rain.

Many buildings described as being built of 'Pentewan stone' are built of similar material from locations such as Polgooth, Sticker, etc. Felsitic elvan dykes have been worked in many different parts of the county; wherever a suitable stone occurs, one frequently finds that it has been quarried along its length, producing a feature like a railway cutting. An elvan which runs from Davidstow Woods to Rock on the Camel estuary was extensively quarried along its length and used for the railway bridges between Camelford and Wadebridge, as well as for many chapels, halls and other buildings. Elvans at Temple and near De Lank Quarry have been similarly worked.

A particularly handsome elvan, with prominent phenocrysts of white orthoclase feldspar and quartz set in a pink fine-grained matrix with spherulitic growths of black tourmaline, was extensively quarried at Tremore, near Withiel. Tremore elvan was quarried by Joseph Treffry in the 1830s to provide stone for the polished slabs used to line the spectacular Porphyry Hall in Place, Fowey.

Greenstone, as was explained earlier, is a convenient term for a variety of basic igneous rocks. Sometimes a dark greenish-blue basic igneous rock will be called 'blue elvan', particularly in west Cornwall, so the term elvan has to be used with care.

Greenstones were some of the earliest building stones to be used in Cornwall. Lower Carboniferous tuffs (tuff = hardened volcanic ash) were used in Norman structures in the Tintagel and Launceston areas. **Cataclews stone** is a dolerite (a basic igneous rock) which was intruded into Upper Devonian rocks at Cataclews Point, about three miles west of Padstow, near Harlyn Bay. It has been used in a number of churches, such as St Merryn and St Petroc, Padstow (*Figure 24f*), and in many of the older buildings in and around Padstow.

A more exotic type of greenstone has been worked at Polyphant, near Launceston, where it has been quarried since Norman times. This was originally intruded as the ultrabasic igneous rock picrite, so basic in composition that it has little or no feldspar, and then subsequently altered so the original olivines and other minerals were converted to a mixture of talc, chlorite and various carbonates. The resulting **Polyphant stone** is quite soft, but is a superb medium for carving and will take a lustrous polish, producing a handsome dark-green shiny surface. Many churches in east Cornwall and farther afield (including Canterbury and Exeter cathedrals) have interior features made of Polyphant stone. The War Memorial adjacent to the West Door of Truro Cathedral is a fine piece of carving in this stone (*Figure 24e*). Launceston Priory and Castle also contain much Polyphant stone, but it does not weather well in exterior use, presumably because it is so soft and porous, and therefore susceptible to frost action.

Greenstones are extensively quarried nowadays as a source of good-quality strong aggregate. They are often also used in the wearing course of main roads, where good skid resistance is needed, which requires that the stone does not become polished as it is worn down by the traffic.

Slate is extensively used in Cornwall for building, both for walls and roofing. It is the most natural material to use for building throughout most of Cornwall outside the granite areas. Delabole Quarry in north Cornwall is the largest and best known source of roofing slate, which has a pleasant silvery-grey colour (*Figure 24g, 18f* and *34*). The large quarry at Delabole is said to have been continuously worked since Tudor times and a considerable export trade was already in existence by 1602. A group of quarries in the Wadebridge area yield large quantities of slate, known as 'St Issey stone', which is used for constructing 'Cornish hedges' alongside roads and for a variety of purposes where a natural stone finish is desired (*Figure 24g*). There are a large number of other small quarries throughout Cornwall which yield slate which is locally used for walling and construction, most of these quarries being in Devonian slate. Many old quarries in the Launceston area yielded roofing and building slate from Carboniferous rocks, but these are now nearly all abandoned.

Sandstone is worked on a small scale from a few localities in north Cornwall, from quarries in the Gramscatho Beds in mid-Cornwall and the Staddon Grits in southeast Cornwall; its main use is as a walling stone.

Limestone is almost absent from Cornwall, apart from a few pockets in the Launceston area, around Veryan and near Trevone, none of which are currently exploited. In the past, limestone from the Plymouth area was brought into the coastal areas of Cornwall for burning to make lime because the deficiency in lime-bearing rocks made for poor acid soils. This was also overcome by using beach sands, largely composed of sea-shells which have been pounded up to a fine sand on the beach by wave action (bioclastic sand) to neutralise their acidity. This type of sand forms the dunes north of Hayle and at Perranporth and many of the beaches on the north coast. A canal was opened in 1823 from Bude to Holsworthy to take this sand to the farms of mid-Devon situated on the sour 'Culm' soils. In places these Quaternary sands are cemented by calcium carbonate, e.g. at Godrevy Point (*Figure 79*), Padstow and Fistral Bay, and have been used as a building stone in some of the older churches, as at Crantock (*Figure 24h*) and Padstow. This must be one of the geologically youngest freestones to be used anywhere in Britain.

Sand and gravel have not been worked extensively although, during the 1960s and 1970s, when alluvial tin was being worked, sand and gravel were an important by-product, as for example at Hydraulic Tin's workings at Bissoe. The bioclastic sands in the Hayle and Padstow estuaries are still worked as a local source of fine sand for building and agricultural purposes.

Bricks have, in the past, been produced in a multitude of small brick kilns, mostly working deposits of clays and weathered material on the surface, scattered all over Cornwall. None are now produced in Cornwall, but brickworks at Millbrook, near Torpoint, and a specialist brickworks at Wheal Remfry, near Indian Queens, were active in the post-war period.

Waste materials from the china-clay industry now represent some of the most widely used raw materials for the construction industry in South-west England. The predominant raw material used in the construction of the architectural award-winning Tate Gallery in St Ives and the Crown Courts in Truro was china-clay waste. In recent years about one million tonnes a year of this waste have been used by the construction industry. The sand is used for concrete and plasters, and is the principal source of raw material for manufacturing concrete blocks, which is the main building medium in Cornwall nowadays. Crushed waste rock from the china-clay industry has also been successfully used as a road foundation material on a number of trunk and main road schemes. China-clay waste has also been used in some major engineering structures, such as the dam wall of Colliford Dam on Bodmin Moor. Unfortunately the total amount of waste produced (about 25 million tons a year) is far greater than the local market can absorb, and the cost of transportation to big cities such as Bristol and London is more than the sand could be sold for.

China-clay waste also has the potential to yield industrial commodities in the future. Mica and feldspar are obvious potential products, and other possibilities include the lithium-rich micas, topaz, rare-earth minerals, tin and wolfram.

Besides china-clay waste, other waste materials from metalliferous mining have been used for constructional use. In most of the mining areas, large cobbles of mining waste, typically slate and quartz-vein material, have been used for rough stone walls and even for domestic cottage construction. In the case of concrete blocks made with a certain type of mine waste, known as 'mundic blocks', this can sometimes turn out to be a liability. Mundic means iron pyrites and this mineral, when exposed to damp, slowly oxidises, releasing sulphuric acid which eats away at the cement, so the block eventually crumbles to dust. This process takes many years to become apparent and in recent years has become a serious problem, with a number of properties having to be demolished as a consequence.

4 The Devonian Period – a great sea covers Cornwall

Most of the sedimentary rocks of Cornwall were laid down during the Devonian and Carboniferous Periods, in the later part of the Palaeozoic Era (*Figure 1*), and are therefore younger than the older Palaeozoic rocks formed during the Cambrian, Ordovician and Silurian Periods in areas such as Wales and the Lake District. Even older rocks are found in the Channel Islands and Brittany, their origins stretching far back into Precambrian time, a thousand million years ago and more. Two rocky reefs off the Cornish coast may be composed of ancient Precambrian rocks – the Eddystone Rocks, 9 miles south of Rame Head, and the Man of War Rocks just off the southern tip of the Lizard. Both are composed of metamorphic rocks called gneiss, which resemble similar ancient rocks seen in the Channel Islands and Brittany.

Adam Sedgwick and Roderick Murchison – one a Professor of Geology at Cambridge and the other later to become the Director of the Geological Survey – visited Devon and Cornwall in 1839 and realised that many of the strata, and the marine fossils they contained, were intermediate in character: older than the Carboniferous but younger than the Silurian, so they proposed the term 'Devonian' to cover the intervening period of time represented by these rocks.

Elsewhere in Britain a thick sequence of red sandstones (the '**Old Red Sandstone**') came between the Silurian and the Carboniferous, and the few fossils these sandstones contained were non-marine, indicating that this extensive sequence was almost wholly laid down in a series of basins and plains on the fringe of a great continent. It was soon realised that the Old Red Sandstone and the marine Devonian sediments of Cornwall and Devon were laid down simultaneously, one on the land and the other under the sea.

An earlier mountain-building episode at the end of the Silurian Period, called the **Caledonian Orogeny**, had formed a mountain range stretching from Scandinavia, through Northern Britain and Scotland, and on through Newfoundland and down the Appalachians (there was no Atlantic Ocean until much later). This mountain range also was the result of two plates colliding. Throughout the Devonian, the Caledonian mountain chain, which also included most of Wales and the Lake District, was undergoing erosion and huge quantities of sediment were being washed out onto the plains on the southern side of the mountains, forming the Old Red Sandstone.

Palaeomagnetic measurements on the iron-bearing minerals in the lavas and sediments of the Old Red Sandstone have shown that Britain lay just south of the equator during the Devonian. The predominant red colour is due to the presence of iron oxides, which suggests that the climate was arid or semi-arid.

We can picture Cornwall for most of the Devonian Period as an area covered by sea, of varying depth, and encompassing some deep basins, lying several hundred miles south of the coastline of the Old Red Sandstone continent. This coastline appears to have lain in the region of north Devon and the Bristol Channel for most of the Devonian although, to begin with, it lay south of Cornwall. Throughout the Devonian Period, from 408 Ma to 360 Ma (Ma = millions of years before present), there was an overall northward retreat of the shoreline in the direction of the South Wales coast of today. In the marginal area of north Devon the sea invaded and receded several times, before finally submerging the area for the last time towards the end of the Devonian, so sometimes the rocks in north Devon are like the Old Red Sandstone further north and sometimes they are like the marine sediments in the rest of Devon and Cornwall.

The Devonian rocks in Cornwall can be divided into two regions (*Figure 5*), separated by the Start-Perranporth Line (SPL). The SPL probably represents an ancient line of weakness, along which there was fault movement during the Devonian. The sediments to the south of it were laid down in deep water, whilst those to the north were deposited in water of variable depth, often quite shallow. Volcanic rocks in the area to the south of the SPL show geochemical affinities with the chemical composition of oceanic crust, whilst those to the north have the geochemical signature of rocks erupted in a continental-plate setting, indicating that the structure and composition of the underlying crust was different.

A table giving the subdivisions of the Devonian strata north of the SPL is shown in *Figure 25*, with the oldest rocks at the bottom and the youngest at the top. The Devonian Period is divided up into a series of *stages*, such as Famennian or Frasnian, mostly named after places in the Ardennes, where the sedimentary sequence has been less deformed than in Cornwall. Fossils are usually the best way to identify to which stage sediments belong.

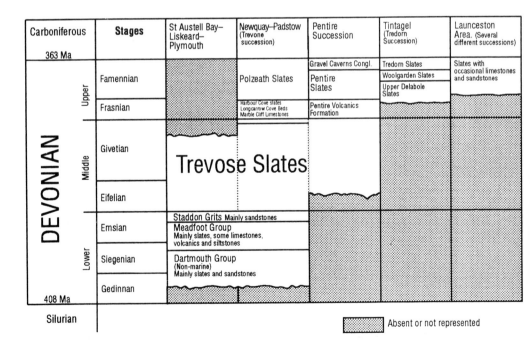

Figure 25 *Sequences of Devonian sedimentary rocks to be found in Cornwall north of the Start-Perranporth Line. Note that the oldest rocks are at the bottom and that the names of the stages (time units smaller than period) are given on the left-hand side.*

THE DEVONIAN TO THE NORTH OF THE START-PERRANPORTH LINE

Lower Devonian (408-386 Ma)

The oldest rocks in Cornwall are the sequence known as the **Dartmouth Group**, named after Dartmouth in south Devon, which are of Lower Devonian age. These are exposed in a band running eastwards from Watergate Bay near Newquay, across Cornwall to Fowey and, on the south coast, are well exposed in Lantivet Bay, further east around Polperro, between Looe and Portwrinkle, and in the southern part of Whitsand Bay out to Rame Head. The distribution is shown on the geological map (*Figure 5*).

The Dartmouth Group strata are usually red, purple and pale green-grey slates and siltstones, with occasional beds of sandstone. Most of the slaty rocks (originally laid down as muds) have developed a strong slaty cleavage as a result of compression during the various phases of the Variscan Orogeny. The red and purple colours of much of the sequence indicate that this is the one part of the Devonian sequence in Cornwall which was laid down under coastal-plain conditions similar to the Old Red Sandstone further north. There are no marine fossils, but primitive freshwater fish are found (*Figure 18a*). The fish are mainly pteraspids and ostracoderms, and one widespread form is known as *Rhinopteraspis cornubica*, originally described from Cornwall. The pteraspids belong to the oldest known order of jawless, heavily armoured fish, probably having a cartilaginous skeleton and possibly related to the present day lamprey. The heavy armour may have been developed in response to predators such as the scorpion-like eurypterids, which reached a size of over a metre at times. The dermal plates of the fish are quite common in places like Watergate Bay, but whole specimens like that shown in *Figure 18a* are much more difficult to find.

We can envisage the landscape at this time as a gently undulating coastal plain, possibly with a few ranges of hills. Wide shallow basins allowed muds (now slates), silts (now siltstones) and sands (now sandstones) to accumulate, these sediments having been washed down by occasional storms from the great continental mass to the north. On the whole the climate would have been hot and fairly arid, but with shallow lakes present for some of the time, their level rising and falling with the extent of the rainfall – much as lakes do nowadays in the interior of Australia. Fish would have lived in the lakes and rivers, and some sparse primitive vegetation would probably have been present, although there is little evidence of this in the fossil record apart from a few spores. As the lakes dried out, the mud cracked in the hot sun and formed polygonal cracks, which have been found at Lantivet Bay.

Further to the south there was probably a shoreline but, apart from a few scraps of Lower Devonian sediment in the structurally complex area of the Roseland coast, we have virtually no knowledge of what lay to the south in Lower Devonian times. A possible reconstruction of the palaeogeography (palaeogeography = ancient geography) during Dartmouth Group times is indicated in *Figure 26a*.

The later part of the Lower Devonian saw the sea invade most of Cornwall; and the resulting marine sediments were named the **Meadfoot Group**, after Meadfoot Beach near Torquay, by W.A.E. Ussher, a 19th-century Geological Survey geologist who mapped much of South-west England. It is understood that the re-mapping of the Plymouth sheet by the Geological Survey will propose that the term 'Meadfoot Group' should include two formations: a lower one named the Bovisand Formation (previously called the Meadfoot Beds), and an upper one named the Staddon Grit Formation – after the long-established term Staddon Grits.

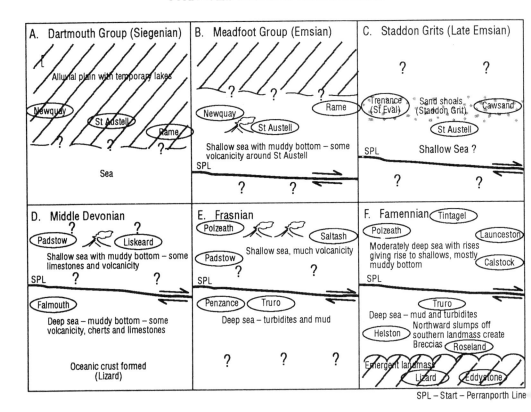

SPL – Start – Perranporth Line

Figure 26 Series of sketch maps to indicate the approximate disposition of land and sea at various times during the Devonian Period.

a   *Dartmouth Group (early part of the Lower Devonian)*
b   *Meadfoot Group (later part of the Lower Devonian)*
c   *Staddon Grits (latest Lower Devonian)*
d   *Middle Devonian*
e   *Frasnian Stage (early part of the Upper Devonian)*
f   *Famennian Stage (later part of the Upper Devonian).*

Note that considerable north-south shortening took place in the Variscan Orogeny after these sediments had been laid down. Land is shown hatched.

The transition from the non-marine Dartmouth Group to the marine Meadfoot Group is seen in a number of places, although these rocks have not been studied in detail in recent years. There may well have been an oscillation between marine and non-marine conditions to begin with; a marine intercalation in the uppermost part of the Dartmouth Group is seen at Bull Cove, near Rame Head, where bands of decalcified sandstone in a grey siltstone sequence have yielded marine fossils such as corals, crinoids and bryozoans, together with non-marine fossils such as ostracoderm fish, perhaps representing a temporary marine incursion. The fossils from Bull Cove represent the earliest Devonian marine fauna known in Britain.

Farther west, at Lantic Bay near Polruan, and at Lusty Glaze near Newquay, the base

42

of the Meadfoot Group is seen to be characterised by the development of limestones. This possibly represents a transitional shallow-water phase, before the rather deeper-water sedimentation of the rest of the Meadfoot Group began. Shallow-water ripple marks are seen on sandstone bedding planes at Lantic Bay. On the south side of Lusty Glaze beach near Newquay, some curious and unusual fossil sponges are found associated with the limestones.

One of the most interesting aspects of these impure limestones is the way they have reacted to metamorphism. At Lantic Bay the intense structural deformation has caused some to be recrystallised into true marble (due to regional metamorphism). Between Newquay and Lantic Bay is the St Austell granite, and some bands of impure limestone have undergone a transformation due to the granite's heat (thermal metamorphism) into a sequence of what are called 'calc-silicate' or 'calc-flintas' rocks, composed of various calcium silicate minerals, such as wollastonite, pyroxene and amphibole; these are produced by the calcium carbonate of the limestone reacting with impurities such as quartz and clay minerals. The main calc-silicate bands are marked on *Figure 5* and have a striking appearance, with alternating white, green and brown bands. Unfortunately, there are very few places where they can now be seen, as most of the old quarries have been filled in.

Pure white marble was encountered in a borehole about half a kilometre west of Duchy Peru mine, near Perranporth, together with a considerable thickness of calc-silicate rocks. An extension of the Cligga Head granite to the northeast at shallow depth is the likely agent responsible for the thermal metamorphism needed to develop these marbles and calc-silicate rocks.

Much of the coast from Newquay to Perran Sands is made up of Meadfoot Group slates, greatly complicated between Holywell Bay and Perran Bay by the deformation associated with the **Start-Perranporth Line** (SPL). This takes the form of a zone of intense shearing associated with the development of a strong cleavage; the most intense deformation is at the south end of Holywell Bay, where small inclusions of quartz show that the movement was dextral.

A shear zone which probably forms part of the SPL showed up in the road cuttings on the Sticker by-pass (A390), with a particularly intense zone of shearing crossing the roadworks in the foundations for a bridge just north of the village of Sticker. Unfortunately, the outcrop is now covered with soil and grass.

On the south coast, the SPL emerges in a less clearly defined zone in the coast between Pentewan (*Figure 27*) and Mevagissey. Some intense zones of deformation can be seen on a stroll around the north side of Mevagissey Harbour. A major WNW-ESE lineament also emerges at Porthpean, and a fault zone associated with an elvan dyke and a dolerite intrusion appears in the cliffs between Black Head and Porthpean, which could all be related to movements along the line.

Most of the Meadfoot Group consists of a rather monotonous series of dark bluish-grey slates with occasional thin beds of siltstone and limestone. The bluish colour is due to fine pyrite, many of the fossils being preserved as pyrite replacements of the original shell. The pyrite indicates stagnant conditions on a sea bottom lacking in oxygen ('anoxic'), which may explain the relative scarcity of fossils. The sediments are commonly finely laminated, which indicates a lack of activity by mud-burrowing creatures, again suggesting hostile conditions on the sea bottom

Away from the structurally complex zone of the SPL, the most interesting area is St

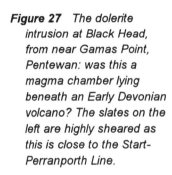

Figure 27 *The dolerite intrusion at Black Head, from near Gamas Point, Pentewan: was this a magma chamber lying beneath an Early Devonian volcano? The slates on the left are highly sheared as this is close to the Start-Perranporth Line.*

Austell Bay, although very little research has been carried out in this area since the beginning of the century. The early geologists, such as Sir Henry De la Beche in 1839 and Charles Peach in 1841, noted the occurrence of fossils from this area and westwards towards Fowey and Polruan. Many of the specimens Peach collected are in the Cornwall Geological Museum in Penzance. A superb *Orthoceras* from Ropehaven was presented to the Royal Cornwall Museum in Truro by Joseph Collins (*Figure 18d*), and the writer has found an *Orthoceras* in a rather different style of preservation at Carlyon Bay. *Orthoceras* was a member of the Ammonoidea, a molluscan family which also includes the goniatites and ammonites that became so widespread in later geological periods. *Orthoceras* was uncoiled, unlike its later relatives, and formed a long straight shell up to half a metre long, which is known from well-preserved specimens found elsewhere to have had bold zig-zag coloured stripes on it. The ubiquitous crinoid ossicles are also found, as well as spiriferid brachiopods, solitary corals and trilobites (*Figure 18c,e*).

Some volcanicity was in progress during Meadfoot times. Between Carlyon Bay and Par, in St Austell Bay, there is a sequence of sediments containing much evidence of volcanicity. *Figure 28* shows large squashed blobs of lava, some vesicular, set in a fine ashy matrix. Some curious beds of what may be pumice or crystal tuff are also seen, as well as some small intrusions of dolerite, mainly in the form of sills. The most peculiar material is a fine-grained yellow rock which at times seems to form bands parallel to the bedding, and at other times looks as if it was intruded into the strata. Similar seams of pale yellow material are found at the north end of Holywell Bay in the Meadfoot

Figure 28   Lower Devonian volcanic material from between Fishing and Spit Points, St Austell Bay. Large stretched-out blobs of lava, in places vesicular, occur in a fine-grained ashy matrix.

Group slates.   It is probably some form of altered volcanic ash, which at times accumulated in depressions in the sea floor, and sometimes was intruded as a fluidised hot material into the soft muds just below the sea bottom.   This volcanicity may be connected with some large intrusions of dolerite which occur in an area running from Trewoon, west of St Austell, to Black Head, on the west side of St Austell Bay (*Figure 27*), formerly exploited in quarries at Tregongeeves, Molingey, etc.; these could possibly represent the magma chambers that fed the volcanoes from below.

Unusual alteration of an intrusion is found at Duporth, also in St Austell Bay. The original rock was most probably a dolerite, which has been altered to a talc-containing material. It appears to have been intruded in the form of a sill. In places it is extremely soft and the unmistakable 'soapy' feel of talc can be sensed when the dry material is rubbed between the fingers. The crumbling cliffs at Duporth are due to this weak material. It is rather similar to the altered picrite at Polyphant; some of the Duporth stone is also said to have been used for interior work. The great Cornish mineralogist, Joseph Collins, described a new mineral from Duporth, which he called 'duporthite'; recent research has shown that duporthite is actually a mixture of talc and chlorite.

Towards the end of Meadfoot times, the sea seems to have become shallower, perhaps with sandy shoals drying out between the tides. These sandy strata are known as the **Staddon Grit Formation**, after Staddon Heights on the east side of Plymouth Sound. The early sandstones of the Staddon Grits show many of the features of having been deposited on the outer fringes of the delta of a river, with wave-produced ripples, cross-bedding and infilled channels. The river feeding the delta appears to have flowed from the north, but what land-mass the river drained is a mystery. A tentative reconstruction of the palaeogeography in Staddon Grit times is given in *Figure 26c*. The upper and younger part of the Staddon Grits seems to represent a line of shoals, developed after the supply of sediment had been cut off. Few fossils are found, apart from occasional worm burrows. The Staddon Grits are fairly resistant rocks and form some of the highest non-granite land in Cornwall. They run in a band across Cornwall from Trenance Point (*Figure 3*), north of Newquay, and then via the high ground of St Breock Downs to Bodmin.

East of Bodmin, the line of the Staddon Grit outcrop is considerably displaced by several major strike-slip faults, including the Portwrinkle and Cawsand faults (see *Figure 5*). The Staddon Grits are well exposed on the foreshore from a point about half a mile east of Kingsand to Picklecombe Point (*Figure 29*). Near the Kingsand end, later weathering during the Permian has caused the grit to be stained by red iron oxides, making the sedimentary structures more visible.

Middle Devonian (386–377 Ma)

The Middle Devonian comprises the Eifelian and Givetian Stages (*Figure 25*). To the east, in Devon, it is characterised by reef limestones and volcanicity, and is full of fossils. Unfortunately, immediately the Tamar is crossed, the limestones are reduced to a few impure bands and the Middle Devonian becomes a rather monotonous sequence of slate, with some volcanicity, known as the Trevose Slates. The palaeogeography in Middle Devonian times is indicated in *Figure 26d*.

The deposition of mud (now slate) in the Liskeard area commenced in the late part of the Early Devonian and continued right through the Middle Devonian. The slates seen in road cuttings alongside the A38 between Menheniot and Trerulefoot will be familiar to many people, and are typical of the Middle Devonian of this area. Fossils have been obtained from the slates and the thin limestones, with trilobites and brachiopods allowing a good correlation with the classic Middle Devonian sequences in Europe. One of the most prolific localities for fossils is near Rosenun Farm, where trilobites such as *Neometacanthus*, *Asteropyge* and *Phacops* and brachiopods such as *Kayserella* and *Athyris*, as well as corals and bryozoans, enable the locality to be placed in the Eifelian Stage. A marked reduction in the abundance of bottom-dwelling fossils occurs in the later part of the Middle Devonian, which suggests a significant deepening of the sea.

Also in the area around Liskeard there are thin horizons of volcanic rocks, mainly in the form of tuffs (volcanic ash) and sometimes pillow lavas. The highly vesicular nature of some of the fragments in the tuffs suggest that they were erupted in relatively shallow water. One rather exotic igneous rock is the ultrabasic augite-picrite at Clicker Tor, formerly exploited in a quarry adjacent to Menheniot station.

There are no exposures of Middle Devonian slates along the southern coast of Cornwall, so we have to travel westwards to the north coast to see them, where they are well exposed in the coastal cliffs from Bedruthan Steps to Trevone. This is shown on the Trevose Head-Camelford geological map (Geological Survey sheets 335 and 336, published as one map), which has been re-mapped by a team from the University of Exeter and recently become available from the Survey.

The Padstow area is the type locality for the Trevose Slates, which are a rather monotonous succession of grey slates. These are seen in the coastal section from Park Head to Trevose Head, where the thickness of the Middle Devonian slates has been estimated to be over 2000 m. The slates have been folded into a major north-facing recumbent fold with a gently southward-dipping axial plane (*Figure 29*).

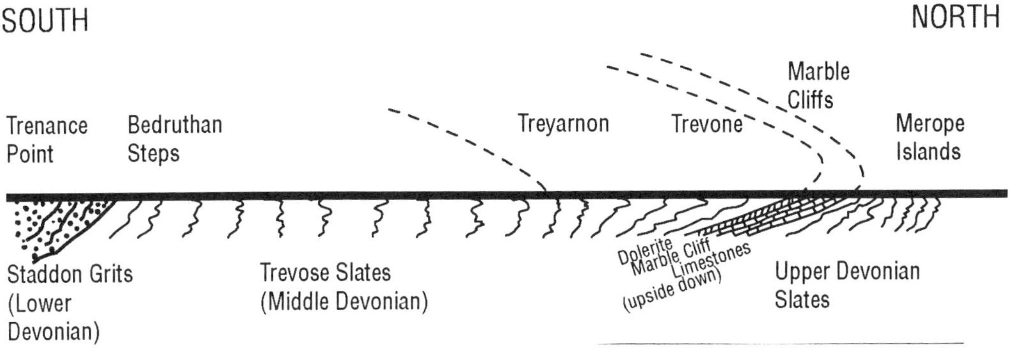

SOUTH   NORTH

Marble
Cliffs

Trenance   Bedruthan   Treyarnon   Trevone   Merope
Point   Steps   Islands

Staddon Grits   Trevose Slates   Dolerite Cliff   Upper Devonian
(Lower   (Middle Devonian)   Marble Cliff   Slates
Devonian)   Limestones
                                                   (upside down)

Figure 29 *Diagrammatic section to illustrate the major fold in Devonian rocks which occupies the north Cornwall coast from Trenance Point to the Merope Islands. The upper part of the fold has been removed by erosion.*

Fossils are found in these slates, such as the ubiquitous crinoid ossicles, as well as fish, dacryoconarids, brachiopods, corals, goniatites and trilobites, but most of the fossils have been replaced by pyrite and lack detail. The Eifelian slates at Bedruthan Steps have yielded a wide range of fossils, especially on Samaritan and Pendarves islands. The Trevose Slates represent a sequence of muds laid down in a fairly deep basinal setting, with the occasional flurry of coarser sediment brought in by a dying turbidity current (such a bed is called a 'distal' turbidite) and beds of volcanic ash.

Towards the top of the Middle Devonian, on the south side of Trevone Bay at Pentonwarra Point, there is an unusually prolific fossil locality, which provides useful dating evidence. Small pyritised goniatites are found here, including the zone goniatite *Maenioceras terebratum*, which places this locality in the late Givetian.

The Middle Devonian succession at Trevone Bay is completed by a change to limestone deposition, and conodont microfossils obtained from three limestone beds exposed near the car park steps on the south side of the bay also indicate a late Givetian age. Dacryoconarids and trilobites are found in the associated slates. The limestones form the lowermost part of the Marble Cliff Beds, which will be described in the next section on the Upper Devonian.

An active quarry near the Royal Cornwall showground, just west of Wadebridge, exploits Middle Devonian slate, much of which is used as 'St Issey stone' to build Cornish hedges alongside new road schemes.

Upper Devonian (377–363 Ma)

Upper Devonian rocks north of the Start-Perranporth Line are restricted to a band running eastwards from around Padstow to the Launceston area. They are mainly slates, although the sequence is generally more varied and interesting than the Middle Devonian. There are some limestones of an unusual type, and much volcanicity.

The Upper Devonian in north Cornwall is characterised by complex structures, which have caused sheets of Devonian and Carboniferous sedimentary and volcanic rocks, originally deposited some distance apart, to be slid into their present position on top of one another, like a stack of sandwiches. So we find a constant repetition of Upper Devonian and Carboniferous sequences; sometimes rocks of the same age in the superimposed sheets are considerably different, due to their having been originally deposited some distance apart. This kind of structure extends right across Devon to the Bickington-Chudleigh area, where it was first recognised by M.R. House and N.E. Butcher working on the Chudleigh area, and by the author working in the Ilsington, Liverton and Bickington area.

Two palaeogeographic reconstructions are given in *Figures 26e* and *26f* for early and late Late Devonian times. However, it must be remembered that folding and thrust faulting have telescoped the north-south distances. One structural expert has calculated that an original distance of 10 km in Late Devonian times was reduced to 3 km after the folding and faulting of the Variscan Orogeny. So, in Late Devonian times, the distance from Newquay to Boscastle could well have been similar to the distance from Newquay to Torquay, making any reconstruction based on the present geography a considerable oversimplification.

The Padstow area is a good place to start, because of the excellent exposures along the coast and in the Camel estuary. It is also one of the most controversial pieces of geology in the whole of South-west England and there have been numerous papers in recent years on this area. Strong feelings have been aroused and I shall have to be careful not to offend anyone!

The **Padstow 'Confrontation'** is one aspect of this debate; it occurs at Gravel Caverns, a short distance north of Polzeath (see *Figure 5*). There is little disagreement that, south of the confrontation line, the sense of tectonic movement that one can deduce from the folds and thrust faults is towards the north, whilst on the north side the sense of movement is towards the south (*Figure 30*). Research has suggested that one explanation could be that the folding and faulting south of the confrontation line belongs to an earlier (?Early Carboniferous) tectonic episode which involved transport towards the north, whilst the movement to the north of the confrontation appears could be a later event, related to the climax of the Variscan Orogeny late in the Carboniferous, which involved transport to the south. Another explanation suggests that, after an early folding episode, the beds to the north of the confrontation were inverted as part

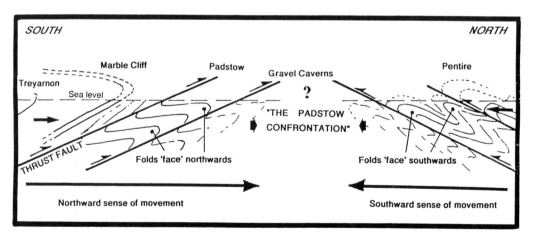

Figure 30 *Diagrammatic section to illustrate the nature of 'The Padstow Confrontation'. On the left all the structures indicate a northward direction of movement, and on the right a southward direction. Where the two systems meet is the Padstow Confrontation, on the coast at Gravel Caverns, half a mile north of Polzeath.*

of a major fold structure, so producing folds of an opposite orientation to those south of the confrontation line. Doubtless the experts will say that I have grossly oversimplified the explanations!

Low-angle faults separate the geology into tectonic 'slices'. As the rocks in each slice may have been deposited many miles apart, before the faulting displaced them, it is necessary first to find out which slice you are in, in order to understand what was going on in the Upper Devonian. Two principal slices have been recognised in the area north and east of Padstow, which contain the Trevone and Pentire successions (*Figure 25*). Still further north, the Tintagel succession is found in the Tredorn Nappe, which belongs to yet another series of thrust slices.

The **Trevone succession** is a continuation of the Middle Devonian succession west of Padstow that was described a few pages back. The **Marble Cliff Beds** mainly belong to the Upper Devonian Frasnian Stage. They are superbly exposed in Marble Cliff, about a quarter of a mile north of Trevone Bay, which consists of an alternating sequence of limestones and slates (*Figure 31*). The 'marble' is not really a true marble, because it has not been fully recrystallised by heat and pressure.

The limestones have yielded conodont microfossils and this has enabled very precise dating of the sequence to be achieved. This shows that the earliest beds are at the top of the cliff, where they are capped by a dolerite intrusion, and the youngest beds are at the bottom of the eastern end of the section, so the whole sequence is upside down (see *Figure 29*). The limestones are mainly composed of crinoidal debris and it is thought that they arrived in place as turbidite flows, presumably derived from a grove of crinoids (sea-lilies) growing on a rise somewhere not too far away. Perhaps periodic severe storms killed the sea-lilies and stirred up the sediment containing the crinoid debris, so that it triggered the formation of a turbidity flow. The background muddy sedimentation, as represented by the slates between the limestone beds, probably represents the 'normal' kind of basinal sedimentation for the locality. The locality is best viewed from the top of the cliffs at the east end.

Basic igneous intrusions, together with the products of volcanic eruptions, are seen at Trevose Head and Stepper Point. At Cataclews Point there is a basic intrusion which was worked in the past as a building stone. A further group of basic intrusions belonging to this period of activity is seen east of the Camel estuary.

Above the Marble Cliff Beds the Upper Devonian is mainly composed of slates. Northwards along the coast between Porthmissen Bridge and Gunver Head, the whole succession of slates is traversed (*Figure 25*), with most of the beds vertical or inverted; volcanic rocks and tuffs are seen in Longcarrow Cove, and small pyritised Frasnian goniatites can be found in bands on the south side of Lower Merope Island.

Towards the top of the Upper Devonian there are bands of purple and green slates (Harbour Cove Slates), which are characteristic of the Upper Devonian as far east as the Newton Abbot area. The two colours are due to the two different oxidation states of iron – red or purple indicates ferric iron and green indicates ferrous iron, reflecting the alternating type of sediment washed into the sea from the adjacent continent. Similar purple and green slates on the north side of Daymer Bay have yielded crushed goniatites such as *Manticoceras* and *Tornoceras*, indicating a Frasnian age, and around Polzeath and New Polzeath the purple, green and dark-grey slates have been shown to be of Famennian age by the presence of ostracods such as *Richterina*. Ostracods are tiny crustaceans enclosed between two shells (bivalved).

Figure 31   *Marble Cliff, near Trevone, where Upper Devonian limestone turbidites alternate with slates. Microfossil age determinations using conodonts show that this whole sequence has been inverted.*

The Pentire succession (see *Figure 25*) has recently been revised, due to new discoveries of microfossils (palynomorphs and conodonts; palynomorphs = fossil spores and pollen) in limestones associated with the Pentire Volcanic Formation. The main difference between the Trevone and Pentire successions is that the latter contains more extensive evidence of volcanicity, together with basic igneous intrusions which are presumably related to this outbreak of volcanicity. The geochemical characteristics of these volcanics indicate that they are typical of intra-plate (not oceanic) volcanism, and the basaltic pillow lavas are magnificently displayed at Pentire Point, most easily seen in some crags alongside the coastal path south of The Rumps. The pillows are highly vesicular and they appear to have had large gas cavities in their centres; the presence of these gas vesicles indicates that these lavas were not erupted into very deep water. Associated with the lavas are water-lain tuffs and basic intrusions. The dolerite intrusions were intruded at a shallow depth below the sea bed into soft unconsolidated sediments, the heat from the intrusions affecting the rocks into which they were intruded; rocks known as adinoles were formed, largely composed of fine crystals of albite feldspar. There appears to have been a multitude of small short-lived volcanoes, rather than a few large volcanic complexes.

The lavas of the Pentire succession are succeeded by more slates – the **Pentire Slate Formation** – which is relatively unfossiliferous and is capped by the **Gravel Caverns Conglomerate**, named after a small cove just north of New Polzeath, where gravel used to be obtained for constructional use. Gravel Caverns Cove also appears to be where the Padstow Confrontation intersects the coast (*Figure 30*). Goniatites found in the conglomerate initially suggested that it was formed in the Frasnian Stage, but recently these goniatites have been shown to be derived from older rocks. So another way of dating using microfossils was attempted and palynomorphs were obtained. These indicated that the conglomerate is much younger and must have been formed at about the time of the Devonian/Carboniferous boundary. The conglomerate contains large pebbles of volcanic rocks, as well as a wide range of other rock types. It may represent the first flush of debris arising from the earliest stage of the Variscan Orogeny (latest Devonian) further south.

The **Tintagel succession** is given in *Figure 25* and a sketch map of the area in *Figure 32*. The Upper Devonian of the Tintagel area is all within the **Tredorn Nappe** and is mostly slate of Famennian age. Few fossils have been obtained from this area. The deformation at Tintagel is particularly intense and this zone of intense deformation extends eastward towards Lydford in Devon. Three sheets 500-1000 m thick, separated by low-angle faults, have been recognised in the Tintagel area and one of these faults runs through the lower part of Tintagel Island (*Figure 33*). All the sheets belong to the Tredorn Nappe, as the succession is similar in all of them.

The oldest formation exposed, the **Upper Delabole Slates**, can be identified by the presence of *Cyrtospirifer verneulli*, which also occurs at the great slate quarry at Delabole, where it is known as the 'Delabole butterfly' (*Figure 18f*). Specimens are often distorted by the deformation which has affected these slates. Occasional thin limestones are found in the Upper Delabole Slates containing crinoid ossicles, bryozoans and brachiopods. The slates have a good regular planar cleavage and were formerly worked in a series of cliff quarries south of Tintagel Island (*Figure 33*), best seen in the vicinity of the Youth Hostel; the history of these quarries is well described in a National Trust pamphlet covering this section of coast.

Inland, the slates continue towards Delabole. In places they have been affected by what is known as the 'greenschist' level of metamorphism. This type of metamorphism is produced by the high pressures and temperatures developed during intense earth movements at depth, which cause the green mineral chlorite (a fine-grained flaky alumino-silicate mineral containing magnesium, *not* chlorine) to form, hence the term 'greenschist'. The metamorphism has made these slates very robust and resistant to weathering, and given them a pale greyish-green hue, weathering a pale silvery-grey, occasional joint surfaces being coated with dark-brown iron oxide. Slate extraction continues to this day at Delabole Quarry (*Figure 34*) and in a number of other inland quarries near Tintagel.

The **Woolgarden Slates** generally have a higher proportion of silty and sandy material. The coarse greyish-green **Tredorn Slates** frequently show small brown spots which are composed of iron oxides derived from the oxidation of original pyrite. The metamorphism was sufficiently intense to form minerals such as orthoclase feldspar and tourmaline, but the source of heat that produced this level of metamorphism is not properly understood.

At the top of the Tredorn Slates a prominent change in colour from greyish-green to black is seen; some geologists have suggested that this marks the Devonian/Carboniferous boundary, as the commencement of the Carboniferous further east appears to be marked by a change to a deeper-water type of sediment. However, there is no fossil evidence to confirm this.

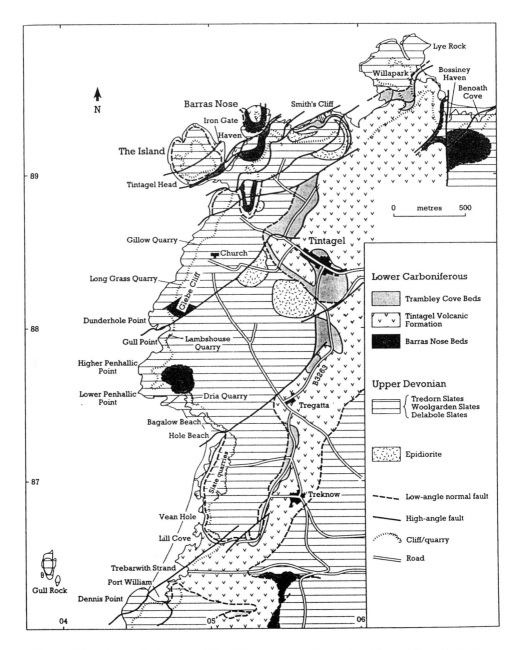

Figure 32 Geological map of the Tintagel area (see also Figure 33). Note the differentiation between the high-angle faults (reverse or normal) and the low-angle normal faults; the latter are referred to as thrust faults by some writers. Map reproduced, with permission, from 'Igneous Rocks of South-West England', published by Chapman and Hall. The original source of the map (Geologists' Association Guide for North Cornwall) is also acknowledged.

Figure 33 *The south side of Tintagel Island. The inset diagram shows how flat-lying faults affected this area and caused the Upper Devonian and Lower Carboniferous sequences to be repeated – see also Figure 32.*

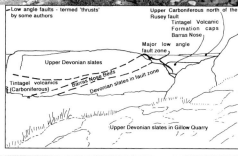

Figure 34 *Delabole quarry in Upper Devonian slates, worked since Elizabethan times.*

The succession in the Launceston-Tamar area. In a sense we have come round in a large circle, having commenced our description of the Middle Devonian rocks in South-east Cornwall. The area was geologically surveyed by a University of Exeter team on behalf of the British Geological Survey around 1980, but no memoir has yet been published, so we have to rely on a few papers written soon after the work was carried out by the geologists involved. Understanding the geological structure of this inland area is handicapped by the shortage of good exposures of rock compared to the magnificent coastal sections.

The research work indicates that the main structural units exposed on the coast can be traced around the northern side of the Bodmin Moor granite. There are indications of much faulting in a NW-SE direction parallel to the eastern side of the granite and there are some sizeable areas of basic igneous rock aligned parallel to the faulting in the same area, which may be partly or wholly Carboniferous in age.

However, once the zone of strike-slip faulting on the east side of Bodmin Moor, usually referred to as the **Plymouth-Cambeak Fault Zone** (see *Figures 5* and *57*) is crossed, the Upper Devonian structure and stratigraphy to the east in the Launceston area takes on a different character. It is as if the Plymouth-Cambeak Fault Zone divides the geology into compartments, suggesting that this fault zone was active from an early date and influenced the deposition of the sediments and the subsequent deformation during the Variscan Orogeny. As we will see later, this fault zone may well have played a key role in accommodating the stresses placed on South-west England during the collision between Normannia and the southern margin of the Old Red Sandstone continent in Lower Carboniferous times. Uplift on the west side of the fault zone may also have brought up rocks from a deeper level in the structural pile, which may help to explain the higher levels of metamorphism seen in the Tintagel area.

Only Upper Devonian sediments are seen in the Launceston area; the geology is made complex by the presence of a multitude of thin tectonic sheets of sedimentary rocks which have been superimposed on one another in a chaotic manner. It is further complicated by the fact that these early sheets were sliced up by a later series of higher-angle thrust faults, which were then, in turn, chopped up by NW-SE strike-slip faults, so we end up with something like a Rubik cube! We also have the problem, just as on the coast, of different successions in different slices, with a fossiliferous shelf sequence in some, and a less fossiliferous but much thicker sequence of basinal slates, like those on the coast, in others. It would appear that the basinal slates (the Kate Brook Formation) form the 'foundation', with the thinner shelf sequences in the overlying slices. These thin slices may represent thin sheets of sediment which have slid northwards down into the basin, as the southern area was uplifted (*see Figure 51* in Chapter 6).

Slates of deep-water origin occupy a considerable part of the area between Launceston and Plymouth. The current re-survey of the Plymouth sheet by the British Geological Survey should throw light on the sequence and structure of the Upper Devonian in this area.

The shallow-water shelf sequence of Upper Devonian rocks in the Launceston area were found to be richly fossiliferous in some of the old quarries, although many of the slate and limestone quarries from which the best specimens were obtained have now been filled in. The strata can be divided into two stratigraphic units: the Petherwin Beds and the Stourscombe Beds. The **Petherwin Beds** are green slates with some thin bioclastic limestones and probably represent shallow-water deposition, perhaps on a sea-floor rise. The **Stourscombe Beds** are probably of the same age and represent deeper-water shelf environments; they may grade laterally into deeper-water basinal slates. Both sets of beds have yielded a rich fauna of goniatites such as *Gonioclymenia, Kosmoclymenia, Cymaclymenia* and *Platyclymenia* as well as trilobites such as *Phacops*, which enabled the early geologists to obtain a good correlation with a group of beds known as the 'Wocklumeria Stufe' in Germany, which are the uppermost beds of the uppermost stage (Famennian) of the Upper Devonian – an appropriate place to end our description of the Devonian north of the Start-Perranporth Line!

THE DEVONIAN TO THE SOUTH OF THE START-PERRANPORTH LINE
(EXCEPTING THE LIZARD)

The Devonian strata south and west of the Start-Perranporth Line (SPL) were laid down in a basin, called the Gramscatho Basin (Gramscatho = an amalgamation of *Gram-*pound and Port*scatho*), which has a very different history to the area to the north of the line. These strata proved to be much more difficult to interpret than those to the north, mainly because early geologists could only find fossils in the structurally complex zone along the Roseland coast. These fossils were typical of Silurian and Ordovician rocks, which suggested that the whole sequence south of the SPL was of similar age, and therefore older than any of the strata we have already described north of it. Reluctantly, these rocks have begun to unlock their secrets, so dating is now possible which shows they were being laid down at the same time as the Devonian strata north of the SPL.

Why is the Gramscatho Basin so different? In recent years, research has suggested that, throughout much of the Devonian, Cornwall was being stretched in a north-south direction, with the result that the SPL could have acted as a normal fault, down-throwing to the south. This seems to have produced much deeper water in the area south of the SPL, in which the sediments of the Gramscatho Basin accumulated. Still further south the stretching may have been so great that the continental crust parted and exposed oceanic crust underneath; that is part of the story of the Lizard, which we will deal with in the next chapter.

Paradoxically, although most of Cornwall appears to have been stretched throughout much of the Devonian, the earliest compressional effects of the Variscan Orogeny were affecting the area south of Cornwall as early as the Middle Devonian; commencing the slow process of collision between the leading edge of the French plate (Normannia), moving up from the south, and the southern side of the Old Red Sandstone continent in Wales, with Cornwall and Devon squeezed in between. A south-dipping subduction zone may have existed between the two plates, but evidence for this is inconclusive.

Before we describe the sediments in the Gramscatho Basin, we must introduce three useful geological terms which describe different parts of a collision structure: **autoch-thon, parautochthon** and **allochthon**. These three parts of a collision structure are shown in *Figure 35*. Let us suppose that there is a mass which is moving from the right-hand side and riding up and over the mass on the left-hand side; the main surface over which the upper mass moves is a major thrust fault. The stationary block on the left which is being overridden is known as the **autochthon**. The actively moving block coming from the right is known as the **allochthon** (think of French, aller = to go). The complicated zone in between the autochthon and the allochthon, with a stack of thrust slices, is the **parautochthon**. These terms have been applied in *Figure 5* to describe the

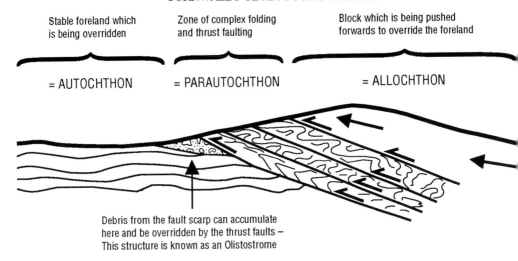

Stable foreland which is being overridden	Zone of complex folding and thrust faulting	Block which is being pushed forwards to override the foreland
= AUTOCHTHON	= PARAUTOCHTHON	= ALLOCHTHON

Debris from the fault scarp can accumulate here and be overridden by the thrust faults – This structure is known as an Olistostrome

Figure 35 Diagrammatic cross-section to illustrate the fundamental components of a major thrust front – allochthon, parautochthon and autochthon. The thrust mass is coming from the right and overriding the stable foreland on the left.

different parts of Cornwall's geology south of the Start-Perranporth Line. Sometimes the thrust sheets, as they remorselessly ground northwards, rode over areas of slumped strata and breccia to produce a structure known as an **olistostrome** (see *Figure 35*).

The Carrick Thrust (*Figure 5*), which runs southwestwards from under Truro to pass just north of Falmouth and intersect the coast near Loe Pool, is interpreted to bound the allochthon to the south from the parautochthon to the north. All the ground southeast of the Carrick Thrust has slid into place from original locations some distance to the southeast. In south Cornwall we do not see any part of the geology which we can confidently call the autochthon.

Sequence in the area SE of the Carrick Thrust (allochthon)

We know little about what happened in early Devonian times in the Gramscatho Basin, but by the end of the Middle Devonian the land forming the southern French Plate (called '**Normannia**' by geologists) was already contributing coarse sediment to the sequence we now see southeast of the Carrick Thrust which, at this time, must have lain some distance south of where it is now. Later in the Devonian, thrust faults allowed the nappes forming the leading edge of the allochthon to override the southern side of the basin (*Figure 36b*), pushing a pile of debris in front, which then triggered massive landslides so that huge rafts of rock and sediment slid down into the deep water of the Gramscatho Basin (*Figure 36c*). This resulted in a chaotic jumble of disrupted strata known as the Roseland Breccia Formation, also known as the Meneage Breccia in the area south of Helford River. Possibly all the material above the Carrick Thrust could have slid into the Gramscatho Basin from somewhere to the south.

The rocks of Normannia were rapidly eroded and shed debris to the north, as rivers carried sediment into the sea and built out deltas. The only bits of Normannia left above sea level now (only just!) are the garnetiferous gneiss of the Eddystone Reef and the hornblende gneiss of the Man of War Reef south of the Lizard, both probably of Precambrian age.

56

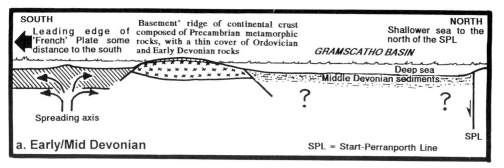

a. Early/Mid Devonian

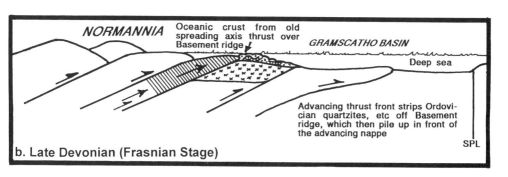

b. Late Devonian (Frasnian Stage)

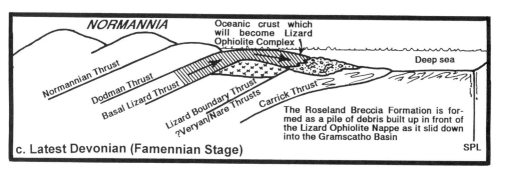

c. Latest Devonian (Famennian Stage)

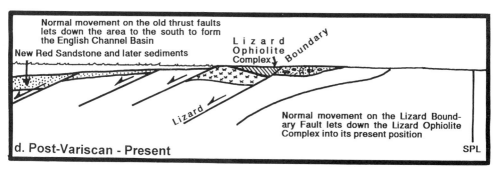

d. Post-Variscan - Present

Figure 36 *A series of cross-sections to show how the geological structure of south Cornwall may have developed. This is just one of many possible interpretations for this highly controversial piece of geology.*

57

Palaeomagnetic measurements have shown that Cornwall was probably just south of the Equator in the Devonian, so Normannia would have been subjected to a tropical climate. Plant fragments have been found in the strata of the Gramscatho Basin, so there was clearly some vegetation. In rocks of similar age in South-west Ireland tracks left by four-legged animals have been found, which are presumed to have been left by some form of primitive amphibian, raising the possibility that similar creatures inhabited the rivers and swamps of Normannia.

The oldest rocks in South-west England (apart from the Eddystone and Man of War Reef) are the Ordovician quartzites found as huge rafts and boulders (olistoliths), up to several kilometres in size, along the Roseland coast. Many notable geologists (such as Lind Hendriks) suggested that the quartzites, although highly deformed, were part of the 'solid' geology; however, the current Geological Survey view is to regard them as part of the Roseland Breccia. Early geologists found easily identified Ordovician trilobites such as *Cheirurus*, *Calymene* and *Phacops* in these quartzites, as well as brachiopods such as *Orthis*, which placed the age firmly in the Llandeilo Stage of the Ordovician. They also found fossils in the Veryan Limestone, which they wrongly identified as belonging to the Silurian Period. As this was the only place in west Cornwall where fossils could be found, it was wrongly assumed by many of the early geologists that all the rocks of west Cornwall were of Ordovician or Silurian age.

The recent Geological Survey work on the Falmouth map has thrown much light on this difficult area. The Roseland Breccia is now seen to form the upper member of a succession of Devonian rocks in the **Veryan Nappe**, which is as follows:

Upper Devonian

> **Roseland Breccia Formation**, including olistoliths of Ordovician quartzite, pillow lavas, etc.

Middle Devonian

> **Carne Formation**, turbidite sandstones, etc.
> **Pendower Formation**, including the Veryan Limestone, cherts, etc.

The upper boundary of the Veryan Nappe is thought to be the Nare Thrust, although the existence of this thrust fault has been doubted by some researchers. The lower boundary is the Veryan Thrust, which passes along the valley which reaches the coast at Pendower Beach.

The lowest member of the succession in the Veryan Nappe is a sequence of slates, cherts and limestone known as the **Pendower Formation**, exposed on the east side of Pendower Beach, immediately east of the Veryan Thrust. The cherts contain abundant radiolaria, which suggests that we are dealing with sediments deposited in a deep-water environment some distance from a source of sediment. The limestones (sometimes known as the Veryan Limestone) were probably emplaced as turbidite flows and contain crinoidal debris and other fossil material. Conodont microfossils indicate that these limestones are of Middle Devonian age (mid to late Eifelian). The overlying **Carne Formation** contains turbidite sandstones, which indicates that a source of sediment was getting closer to the area.

Pebbly sandstones belonging to the Carne Formation are also exposed on the west side of the Fal Estuary at Menaver Beach. Here a channel contains a conglomerate with clasts of granite, quartzite, vein quartz, mica-schist, mudstone and sandstone.

Further west, at Church Cove on the west side of the Lizard, medium- to thick-bedded turbidites are seen, also probably belonging to the Carne Formation, with well-developed sole markings (flute marks and grooves) and isoclinal folding.

Overlying the Carne Formation is the **Roseland Breccia Formation** (*Figure 37*), including what was formerly known as the Meneage Breccia. This chaotic jumble of rock types, including the enormous rafts of Ordovician quartzite, must have slid off the northern (probably submarine) slopes of Normannia, indicating that the source of the sediment was getting very close. So, the increasing proximity of Normannia is indicated by the sediments becoming coarser and more chaotic as Devonian time progressed. Finally, the movement on the thrust faults caused the breccia to be overridden and buried beneath the nappe above, a common feature of olistostromes world-wide.

The Ordovician quartzites in the Roseland Breccia are best seen in a series of quarries immediately south of the village of Carne, accessible by the footpath that leads down to Paradoe Cove. Bold crags of quartzite are seen here (*Figure 38*) and also in the cliffs below. Large fold structures in the quartzite are seen in the cliffs (best seen from the sea). The length of the quartzite outcrop, which stretches back under the village of Carne, may be as much as a kilometre. These small local stone quarries are also said to be the site of wartime efforts to obtain high-purity silica for the manu-facture of electronic components.

The Roseland Breccia is exposed along much of the coast between Pendower Beach and Mevagissey, with the exception of Nare Head and The Dodman. In Veryan Bay there are conglomerates, probably belonging to the Roseland Breccia, composed of pebbles (clasts) of granite and metamorphic rocks, best seen at Jacka and Caragloose Points. The clasts can be studied under the petrological microscope, which tells us a great deal about their mineralogy. They probably came from Normannia and represent samples of the rocks which formed this mysterious land. This suggests that the geology of Normannia had a great deal in common with the geology of northern Brittany and the Cotentin Peninsula in Northern France, for similar metamorphic rocks and Ordovician quartzites are found there.

Still further east, the Roseland Breccia is well displayed in the cliffs to the east of Gorran Haven where rafts containing pillow lavas and radiolarian cherts can be seen at Great Perhaver Point, and massive crags of Ordovician quartzite in the breccia in the cliff above Great Perhaver Beach. A quarry at Tubb's Mill, north of St Michael Caerhays, also shows pillow lavas. The breccia is also seen in the Meneage, north of the Lizard, between Porthallow and Nare Point. In Nelly's Cove, a short distance north of Porthallow, pillow lava is seen and a wide range of other rock types, including granite, limestone and sandstone.

The interesting thing about all these volcanic rocks in Roseland is that their chemistry indicates that they are of a type which is usually associated with *M*id-*O*cean *R*idge *B*asaltic volcanism – we say it has 'MORB' affinities. This suggests that these volcanics originated from an area underlain by oceanic crust some distance to the south, possibly outside the Gramscatho Basin proper, and the breccia formed as a debris pile in front of the Lizard ophiolite as it slid down into the basin. The interpretation of the structural evolution of south Cornwall shown in *Figure 36* is based on such an origin.

The early work by the local geologist Lind Hendriks envisaged the Roseland area to be composed of a series of *gravity-driven* nappes (see *Figure 36*), and it is worth quoting from her extraordinarily perceptive 1949 paper:

Figure 37 *Roseland Breccia on the beach near Carne. Clasts of limestone and other rocks in a muddy matrix probably represent a major submarine slump.*

"The view of nappe structure here visualised is first, the formation of a (ge)anticline, and the development from it of a great recumbent fold gradually growing into an overfold, of which the middle limb becomes sheared out and replaced by a horizontal thrust. The forward sliding movement is retarded only by the friction on the underside. In this way great blocks of country are driven forward and are themselves responsible for the recumbency and forward-drag below them of fold after fold. The conditions preparatory to such folding are those under which the Cornish flysch [a turbidite sequence of muds and sandstones] *was laid down: deposition in an orogenic trough in front of a new range."*

The Veryan Nappe is not by any means the top of the stack of nappes separated by thrust faults. Above the **Nare Head Thrust** there are basic volcanic rocks including the magnificent pillow lavas of Nare Head itself (*Figure 15*), and then there is the **Dodman Thrust** forming the upper boundary of that nappe, with the phyllitic slates of the Dodman above. These are resolutely unfossiliferous, so their age is uncertain.

The next unit above in the stack of nappes is believed to be the **Lizard**, which involves at least two nappes; this is described in the next chapter. Above that comes the **Normannian Thrust**, with the rocks of Normannia above. The full set of nappes is probably not present anywhere, as nappes may thin out and disappear, or completely change their character.

The structures in the rocks under the sea bed off south Cornwall have been studied by means of offshore seismic and magnetic geophysics. Low-angle features have been interpreted to be thrust faults dipping southwards to depths of up to 17 km. Westwards a similar set of seismic features can be identified south of the Isles of Scilly.

Below the Veryan Nappe is the **Carrick Nappe**, which is the lowest in the stack of

Figure 38 A crag of Ordovician quartzite at Carne. Large rafts of this quartzite slid down into the deeper part of the Gramscatho Basin to become incorporated into the Roseland Breccia.

nappes and is bounded below by the Carrick Thrust. The rocks in this nappe are a thick sequence of sandstone turbidites interbedded with grey slates, known as the **Portscatho Formation** (often described in the literature as part of the Gramscatho Formation or Gramscatho Beds), estimated to be 5400 m thick. These are well exposed in the cliffs and foreshore of the western part of Gerrans Bay.

Turbidite units with graded bedding and flute casts on the base of the bed can be seen on the foreshore about 500 m west of the access road at the western end of Pendower Beach (*Figure 39*). Plant fossils discovered in thin wispy coaly seams from this locality in the 1920s were named *Dadoxylon hendriksae*, after Lind Hendriks. (*Figure 40*). This was a primitive Devonian land plant which appeared to consist of primitive rhizomes and shoots growing in a swamp environment; rafts of vegetation must have been washed out by rivers draining the Normannian land-mass to the south, which then sank to become buried in the sediments on the sea bottom. It was originally thought to indicate a Middle Devonian age, but more recent work on the microfossils (miospores and acritarchs) has indicated that the upper part of the Portscatho Formation is younger, most probably Upper Devonian.

Studies of the chemistry and mineralogy of the sandstones in the Portscatho Formation suggest they were derived from an area with volcanic activity fringing a continental land-mass composed of ancient metamorphic rocks – another glimpse of Normannia.

There are minor sequences of purple and green siltstones and mudstones, together with calcareous sandstones, in the Portscatho Formation of the St Mawes area. The low cliffs around the estuary of the Helford river are also composed of slates and sandstones belonging to the Portscatho Formation, perhaps best seen in the small beaches at the southern end of Trebah and Glendurgan gardens.

Figure 39 *Turbidite units in the Portscatho Formation, Pendower Beach. The pale-grey rock is sandy, the dark grey muddy; the grading in each unit (coarse sandy particles at bottom, finer mud particles at top) indicates that this sequence is the right way up.*

On the western side of the Lizard peninsula, the Portscatho Formation is seen in the cliffs from Loe Pool to Jangye-ryn. Intense folding associated with the presence of the Carrick Thrust is seen just south of Loe Pool (*Figure 41*). Further south, at Jangye-ryn, medium to thin-bedded turbidites are seen, with some fine large angular folds (*Figure 43*), which attracted the attention of the early geologists who visited the area; Sedgwick in 1822 found it "difficult to account for by the action of mere mechanical forces", because the processes of folding were not properly understood at that date. Some of the early fossils of *Dadoxylon* wood came from here. A steep fault at the south end of the beach brings in the Carne Formation, thereby cutting out the Veryan Thrust.

x 100. Transverse Section.   x 100. Radial longitudinal section.

Figure 40 *Wood of the plant fossil* Dadoxylon hendriksae, *from the type locality at Pendower Beach, showing transverse and radial sections. Drawn by E.M.L. Hendriks.*

Figure 41 *Intense folding in the Portscatho Formation, Loe Pool (south side). The intensity of the deformation is probably due to the proximity of the Carrick Thrust.*

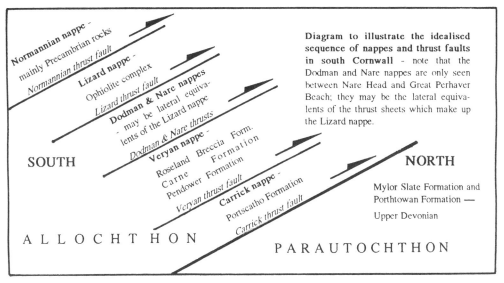

Figure 42 *The idealised sequence of nappes and thrust faults in south Cornwall. The Dodman and Nare nappes are only seen between Nare Head and Great Perhaver Beach—these may be lateral equivalents of the thrust sheets which make up the Lizard Nappe, although the relationship of the Lizard Complex to the rest of Cornwall is still highly controversial.*

Figure 43 *Angular folds in alternating turbidite sandstones and slates of the Portscatho Formation, Jangye-ryn Cove, near Gunwalloe, on the west side of the Lizard (archival photograph with Captain Richards, courtesy of the Royal Cornwall Museum).*

A magnificent inland exposure of the Portscatho Formation has recently been created by the road-widening scheme on the A39 east of Truro, at Woodcock Corner. Towards the upper end of the exposure several southward-dipping thrust faults are seen, which may be related to the Carrick Thrust, which is mapped to pass only a short distance (500 m) to the north. The beds are mainly a sequence of thin turbiditic siltstones and slates.

Sequence in the area NW of the Carrick Thrust (parautochthon)

Two formations are recognised in this area, the Mylor Slate Formation and the Porthtowan Formation. These are often described in the literature as part of the Gramscatho Group and may be partly of the same age, but were deposited in slightly different submarine environments. The Porthtowan Formation is interpreted as a basinal or rise deposit, whilst the Mylor Slates comprise rise, slope and possibly outer shelf deposits. The dating of the Mylor Slates was unknown until microfossils (palynomorphs) were found in samples of slate from the Mount Wellington mine, obtained shortly before the mine closed in the 1970s. These indicate an uppermost Famennian (Upper Devonian) age, close to the Devonian/Carboniferous boundary.

The **Porthtowan Formation** is well exposed along the coast from Hayle to Perranporth. It consists mainly of grey and greyish-green slate with some thin beds of sandstone and siltstone, probably laid down by turbiditic flows. There is little evidence of volcanicity in the Porthtowan Formation.

At Godrevy Point, on the east side of St Ives Bay, folded slates with regular beds of sandstone and siltstone are seen. A fine pair of isoclinal folds is present on the foreshore close to the access from the coastal footpath (*Figure 8d*). Similar rocks are also seen west of the Hayle estuary at Lelant Towans and on the east side at Black Cliff.

The **Mylor Slate Formation** is well displayed on the south coast in the cliffs

Figure 44   *Folding of thin turbidite slates and siltstones in the Mylor Slates at Porthleven, now hidden behind concrete sea defences.*

between Porthleven and Loe Pool (*Figure 44*).   The folding becomes particularly intense towards Loe Pool, with the Carrick Thrust believed to intersect the coast via the Loe Pool valley.   Closer to Porthleven, a number of small dolerite intrusions are seen.

Mylor Slates are also seen around the shores of Mount's Bay as far west as Mousehole.   Sedimentary breccias are found in this area at locations such as Stackhouse Cove and Long Zawn.   It is believed that these breccias were formed soon after deposition by some form of submarine slumping.

There is much evidence of igneous activity in the Mylor Slates in Mount's Bay and between the Carnmenellis and Land's End granites, as well as in the narrow strip of Devonian rocks on the north side of the Land's End granite.   This was clearly an area of intense volcanic activity in the Late Devonian, with pillow lavas, indicating submarine eruptions, together with pyroclastic rocks such as tuffs and agglomerates. Short-lived volcanic islands and shoals could have formed at times.   The volcanicity is of a similar age to the Upper Devonian Pentire Volcanic Formation of north Cornwall. The chemistry of the Penwith igneous rocks is intermediate between the Mid-Ocean Ridge Basalts (MORB) which form the pillow lavas of Roseland, and the Pentire volcanics, which have the characteristics of basalts erupted in a continental-plate environment.

Some of the intrusions are relatively coarse-grained gabbros and dolerites, indicating slow cooling and intrusion at depth, as at Cudden Point east of Marazion.   Other intrusions are fine grained and grade up into crude pillow structures with vesicular margins.   One such mass, which lies within the area affected by heat from the Land's End granite (the metamorphic aureole) between Mousehole and Newlyn, has been exploited in the large Penlee quarry. The metamorphism has converted the basic intrusion into a very tough rock which is valued for concrete and roadstone.

A particularly interesting occurrence is Great Hogus reef, exposed at low tide on the beach between St Michael's Mount and Marazion. This shows agglomerates and water lain tuffs; there are two beds of agglomerate and some of the larger fragments of vesicular lava are up to 50 cm long, so are unlikely to have travelled far from the vent. The grading in the beds of agglomerate suggests the beds are the right way up. The degree of vesicularity (vesicles = gas bubbles in the lava) indicates that this volcanic activity cannot have been in any great depth of water.

A narrow band of Mylor Slates borders the Land's End granite on the north side. It also contains many greenstone masses, both intrusive and extrusive. Pillow lavas are seen northwest of St Ives at Carrick Du (at the western end of Porthmeor Beach). Many of the basic sills near St Ives were probably originally dolerite or gabbro, but grade upwards into crude pillow structures and have amygdaloidal margins (= vesicles infilled with later-formed minerals), indicating that the magma was probably intruded into soft wet sediments just below the sea floor.

All the Mylor Slates and associated rocks in this strip on the north side of the granite have been affected by the heat from the granite (thermal metamorphism). The first sign of this in the slates is spotting, due to the clumped growths of the mineral chlorite and carbonaceous matter. Nearer to the granite the mineral andalusite is found, with cordierite in the zone closest to the granite. Strongly baked slates and siltstones are called **hornfels**. Close to the granite the hornfels may have been affected by boron-containing fluids emanating from the granite, producing a striking black and white rock with alternating bands of tourmaline and quartz (*Figure 8c*). The greenstones react to thermal metamorphism by producing tough rocks which are rich in various types of amphibole and pyroxene.

The rocks of the metamorphic aureole are almost as hard as or even harder than the granite itself, and are traversed by mineralised veins which contain ores of tin and copper. This produces some very striking scenery, where the crenellated cliffs can be directly related to rocks which offer greater or lesser resistance to erosion by the sea. The greenstones are some of the hardest, and form headlands; the granite is probably slightly less hard, and the hornfels is the least hard. Major coastal inlets are often formed where alteration along veins and fracture zones has weakened the greenstones and the granites.

As far as we know the youngest beds of the Mylor Slates are latest Fammenian in age, although it is just possible that they could be earliest Carboniferous. There are no younger beds in the Gramscatho Basin. Soon after, in the Early Carboniferous, the area was subjected to the deformation and mountain building which took place in the first phase of the Variscan Orogeny. This will be described in Chapter 6, once we have taken a look at the extraordinary tale of the Lizard.

5 *The curious tale of the Lizard – and a vanished ocean*

The early geologists thought that the rocks of the Lizard were older than the rocks in the rest of Cornwall, because the intensely deformed and recrystallised metamorphic rocks that they found there, similar to those found in ancient metamorphic massifs, suggested a great age. We now know that the igneous rocks of the Lizard are probably no older than the rest of the Devonian rocks in Cornwall, but were subjected to a relatively high temperature metamorphism soon after they were formed, possibly because they were involved in faulting and thrusting before they had cooled from their original igneous temperatures. In the early part of the Devonian, there appears to have been an area of ocean to the south of Cornwall, called the **Rheic Ocean**, but we have little idea how wide this ocean was, or even where it was.

The crust below the oceans

Oceanic crust is formed at a spreading axis by a rising convection current of hot material in the mantle (*Figure 19*), and much of the new oceanic crust is made by the repeated injection of dykes at the spreading axis. As the new crust is pushed away from the spreading axis by more new crust being formed, it cools and becomes inert oceanic crust on which in time a layer of sediments will slowly build up. The **layers** which make up oceanic crust can therefore be summarised as follows (in descending order):

6. A **layer of sediment** composed of fine clay particles washed in by ocean currents, volcanic ash from distant eruptions and the remains of open-ocean organisms such as radiolaria.

5. **Pillow lavas** formed by magma injected up the dykes in layer 4 below. These have a characteristic MORB (Mid-Ocean Ridge Basalt) chemical composition.

4. A **sheeted-dyke complex** – as the crust is pulled apart at the spreading axis, it cracks and allows magma to squirt up from below, forming dykes (*Figure 45*). These are oriented perpendicular to the spreading and also show MORB geochemistry.

3. Intrusions of **gabbro** (a coarse-grained basic igneous rock), often showing layering due to the heavier crystals settling out as the magma crystallises. The large intrusions of gabbro feed the dykes in layer 4.

2. Intrusions composed of heavy crystals which settled out from the layer above – **'ultrabasic cumulates'** (ultrabasic = an igneous rock very low in silica and largely composed of minerals rich in iron and magnesium; also termed *ultramafic*).[4]

1. Intrusions of ultrabasic magma of **peridotite** type, including rock types known as dunites, harzburgites, lherzolites, etc., which are mainly composed of olivine and pyroxene. This is the material which also forms the earth's mantle below the crust, and is only rarely seen at the surface.

There is an important change in seismic velocity of the rocks, known as the **Mohorovicic discontinuity,** or 'Moho' for short, which typically lies between layers 2 and 3, at a depth of about 20 km under the continents, but at a shallower level under

Figure 45 *Basic dyke in the gabbro of the Lizard Complex, on the shore between Coverack and Porthoustock.*

areas with oceanic crust. The Moho marks an important change in the physical state of the rocks – below it rocks can flow more easily by plastic deformation.

Structure of the Lizard Complex

The Lizard Complex is a series of slices of Early Devonian oceanic crust. Put simply, as the Rheic Ocean which occupied the gap between the southern Normannian Plate and the northern Laurasian Plate was eliminated by the two plates colliding, a series of slices of the oceanic crust, still hot from being formed, somehow became caught up in the thrust faulting and were trapped between thrust slices composed of Devonian strata and other older rocks. These slices were then brought up to a high level in the continental crust by further faulting and thus gives us a rare opportunity to look at material from the mantle and the vicinity of the Moho. Such a structure is known to geologists as an **ophiolite complex** and the Lizard Complex is the best example of an ophiolite in Britain. However, the northern boundary of the complex is formed by a normal fault downthrowing to the south. This fault extends from Polurrian in the west to Porthallow in the east; a parallel east-west normal fault may extend inland from Porthoustock. Both faults are much later than the thrust faulting and are probably part of the extensional faulting that took place after the Variscan Orogeny.

A sketch map of the geology of the Lizard is shown in *Figure 46*, and a conjectural cross-section through the Lizard Complex and Gramscatho Basin in *Figure 47*.

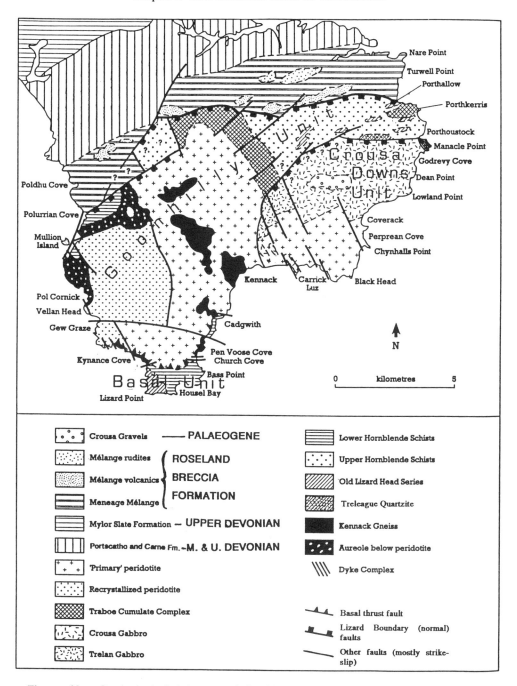

Figure 46 *Geological sketch map of the Lizard, showing the three structural units (Crousa Downs, Goonhilly and Basal) and the various rock types involved; see also Figure 47 for a cross-section. Map reproduced, with permission, from 'Igneous Rocks of South-west England', published by Chapman and Hall. The contribution of Alan Bromley to our understanding of the structure of the Lizard is also acknowledged.*

The Lizard Complex is composed of three thrust sheets (*Figures 36* and *47*), although recent research suggests there may be only two:

Crousa Downs Unit This is the uppermost thrust slice, which is seen on the east side of the Lizard and shows Layers 1-4. The upper layers are cut out by the thrust faulting, although the Treleague Quartzite (Layer 6) and the Mullion pillow lavas (Layers 5 and 6) may be part of this unit.

Goonhilly Downs Unit The main part of the Lizard Complex, this is more highly metamorphosed than the Crousa Downs Unit. It consists mainly of Layer 1 material and is overlain to the northeast by the Traboe Hornblende Schists (Layer 2) and other metamorphic rocks. At its base a more acidic metamorphic rock is found, called the Kennack Gneiss.

Basal Unit This unit is found only along the southern margin of the Lizard Complex and is composed mainly of high-grade metamorphic rocks such as the Landewednack Hornblende Schists, the Old Lizard Head Series and the Man of War Gneiss. It probably represents highly metamorphosed lavas (Layer 5) and sediments (Layer 6), although recent research now suggests that the Man of War Gneiss may be a Precambrian metamorphic rock.

One of the special features of the Lizard Complex is that in parts it has suffered far more intense metamorphism than any other rocks in South-west England. This metamorphism is at its most intense in the Basal Unit of the complex, although the Goonhilly Downs Unit also contains gneiss and schist (see above). Recently published radiometric ages suggest that the oceanic crust was formed at a spreading axis in the Early Devonian and that the metamorphism took place as this crust was broken up and thrust northwards, incorporating some non-oceanic crustal material in the process, in the Mid/Late Devonian (see *Figure 36*, page 57).

Another complicating factor is that most of the ultrabasic rocks, to a greater or lesser extent, have also been subjected to a low-temperature process known as *serpentinisation*, which involves the original anhydrous minerals taking up water and forming new minerals which are stable in the presence of circulating groundwater.

Figure 47 The perplexing structure of the Gramscatho Basin and the Lizard Complex is indicated in this cross-section (see also Figure 36).

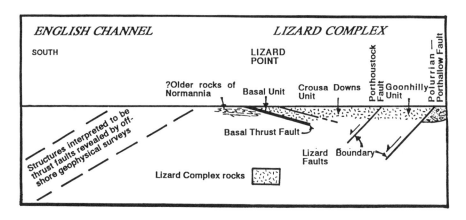

Sometimes, when carbon dioxide is present, the serpentine itself is further altered to a mixture of talc and iron-rich magnesium carbonate. These talc deposits were one of the few economic resources to have been exploited in the Lizard. At Gewgraze (north of Kynance Cove), talc was worked in the 18th and early 19th centuries and was used in the manufacture of porcelain, before the potential of china clay for use in a wider range of porcelains was understood. Traces of the old workings can still be seen; shipments were sent up to the Potteries for tableware manufacturers such as Wedgwood to use.

A little copper was also produced from the Lizard rocks, sometimes in the native form (pure metal), as well as construction aggregate and the serpentine used for manufacturing ornaments.

So, next time you handle a piece of Lizard serpentine, remember that it started off its life in the earth's mantle deep under a vanished ocean!

Key locations

Let us now look in more detail at some key locations in the Lizard Complex. To assist the reader in understanding what is to be seen, locations which show Layer 1 rocks will be described, then locations which show Layer 2, and so on.

Layer 1 locations – the mantle peridotites

These can be subdivided into those which show something of the original rock as formed in the mantle, and those which have been extensively altered by serpentinisation. One of the best places to see relatively unaltered mantle peridotites is at Coverack, in the vicinity of the harbour and at Dolor Point, although even these have been serpentinised to some extent. These dark-green rocks are composed of olivine and pyroxene; they are known as harzburgites and lherzolites.

Northwards across Coverack Beach there are some dunites and the transition to the gabbros of Layer 3 is seen, but the cumulate rocks of Layer 2 are not well represented here. In the centre of the beach, gabbros and peridotites are interbanded and the Moho at the time the oceanic crust was being formed must have lain at about this level. The northern end of the beach is formed of the paler coarse-grained gabbros of layer 3.

One of the best places to see Layer 1 is at Kynance Cove (*see the painting by J.C. Uren, on the back cover*). Two types of Layer 1 material are seen here. The east side of the cove is formed by 'bastite serpentine' (best seen alongside the footpath leading down from the National Trust car park); this is the least deformed type and was

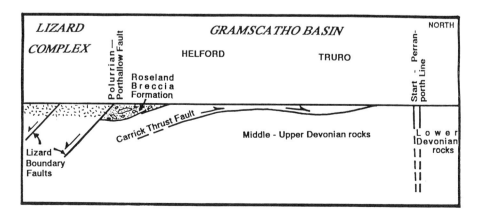

originally a coarse lherzolite. Bastite is the name for the prominent pyroxene crystals. A fault separates the bastite serpentine from the tremolite serpentine, which forms most of the rocks seen at sea level in the cove itself. This is a highly deformed serpentine which was possibly derived by metamorphism of the bastite serpentine, or from some other rock. It contains the amphibole mineral tremolite, and is the material mainly used in the manufacture of serpentine ornaments. There are granite dykes at Kynance, which commonly show a partial change to talc.

Layer 2 locations – the 'cumulate' rocks

The most extensive development of cumulate rocks is known as the Traboe Cumulate Complex, unfortunately not exposed on the coast. The nearest material to this is seen on the coast about half way between Porthallow and Porthkerris Point. This exposure is close to the base of the Lizard Complex, where metamorphism is at its most intense, so we are dealing with rocks that are highly deformed and have been metamorphosed into hornblende schists. In spite of this, banding can be seen at several locations in the section, indicative of the development of cumulates.

Some dunite is seen at the Porthallow end of the section. This section is of great interest because, at the Porthallow end, the contact between the rocks of the Lizard and the Devonian Roseland Breccia is seen. The latter forms the northern side of Porth-allow Cove, and on the south side a band of metamorphic gneiss can be seen underlying the ultrabasic Layer 2 rocks. The main fault separating the Lizard Complex from the Roseland Breccia is a normal fault on the south side of the cove, dipping at 45° southwards (see *Figure 47*).

Layer 3 locations – the gabbros

The gabbros of the Lizard are best seen on the eastern side of the Lizard in the Crousa Downs thrust slice. One of the best locations has already been mentioned at the north end of Coverack Beach and northwards towards Lowland Point. The gabbro here sometimes shows the development of pale, coarse feldspar rich zones, which are termed 'plagiogranites'. Dean Quarry, the large aggregate quarry near St Keverne, is in the gabbro of Layer 3 and shows both fine-grained and coarse 'pegmatitic' types of gabbro.

At Carrick Luz, crushed and recrystallised gabbros are seen containing deformed and serpentinised masses of peridotite. The gabbro may here be in the form of a large dyke, cut by intense shear zones which may represent a transform fault associated with the spreading axis. At both localities feeder dykes associated with Layer 4 are seen.

Layer 4 locations – the sheeted-dyke complex

The best location to see the sheeted-dyke complex of the Lizard is between Manacle Point and Porthoustock (*Figure 45*). Several generations of dykes are present, show-ing clear cross-cutting relationships. The earlier dykes have a MORB chemistry and are clearly related to the gabbros. The later cross-cutting dykes are not so clearly MORB-related and may indicate the proximity of volcanic island-arc magmatism at the edge of a continental plate. Some of the dykes show a chilled margin (resulting from contact with cool rock, so that it is finer-grained or even glassy) on one side only, which is a typical feature of sheeted-dyke complexes in ophiolites. At Porthoustock Point the dykes locally form about 80% of the mass of rock, with only thin layers of gabbro separating them. The sequence in the Crousa Downs Unit is terminated at this point and we do not see any Layer 5 or 6 material on the east coast of the Lizard.

Layer 5 locations – the pillow lavas

The pillow lavas of the Lizard Complex are only seen at two locations, and at both the relationship to the main part of the ophiolite is not clear.

At Lizard Point the **Old Lizard Head Series** is thought to be a highly meta-morphosed series of sediments. Associated with this are the **Landewednack Hornblende Schists**, which are interpreted to be metamorphosed basaltic lavas with a MORB composition. These rocks are seen below the lighthouse where the meta-morphism of the basaltic lava has produced a rock known as an amphibolite. Pillow structure cannot be deciphered because of intense deformation, but isoclinal folding can be seen in places.

Pillow lavas are beautifully displayed on Mullion Island, and are relatively un-metamorphosed. Conodonts have been obtained from siliceous limestones resting on top of the pillow lavas and indicate an Upper Devonian (Frasnian) age. However, the relationship with the rest of the Lizard Complex is not clear, although these lavas are juxtaposed against the western side of the Lizard Complex. They are similar to the pillow lavas seen in the Roseland Breccia, notably at Nare Head and Great Perhaver Point near Gorran Haven, which also show MORB affinities. They are thought to represent large masses of the former ocean floor of the Rheic Ocean, which slid down into their present position during the formation of the Roseland Breccia in Late Devonian times.

Layer 6 locations – the oceanic sediments

As we have already mentioned, the Old Lizard Head Series may represent schists formed from volcanic-derived sediments which originally rested on top of the oceanic crust of the Rheic Ocean, and were then intensely metamorphosed when the Lizard ophiolite was thrust into its present position. The limestones of Frasnian age associated with the Mullion pillow lavas were mentioned above. There is, however, another area of sediments possibly involved in the Lizard Complex, namely the Treleague Quartzite. Some authors have interpreted this as a large raft or rafts of quartzite contained within the Roseland Breccia; another interpretation is that it has been downfaulted into its present position, and that it originally rested on top of the Lizard oceanic crust. The occurrence of basic igneous dykes cutting the quartzite, similar to those in Layer 4 of the Lizard Complex, is cited as possible evidence of this. Unfortunately the quartzite is nowhere exposed on the coast, so it is difficult to be sure which interpretation is correct.

Some distance away to the east, in between Little and Great Perhaver Beaches, just east of Gorran Haven, there is a thick succession of pillow lavas associated with sediments composed of volcanic debris and chert. Although this mass probably represents a large raft of material which slid down into the basin, it nevertheless does give an idea of what the sediments on the floor of the Rheic Ocean were like.

So, in the Lizard, we see slices of oceanic crust formed at a spreading axis sometime in the Late Devonian. Before these had time to cool they became involved in the earth movements associated with the earliest phase of the Variscan Orogeny.

Because of their different origin, the rocks of the Lizard have a chemistry quite distinct from those in the rest of Cornwall and this is reflected in the unusual present-day plant communities, especially the heaths, which are to be found on this southernmost part of Britain.

6 The Carboniferous Period in Cornwall – deep seas and the beginnings of mountain building

We now move on to consider the next period of geological history – the Carboniferous. Elsewhere in Britain the Carboniferous generally divides quite neatly into two distinct parts: the Lower Carboniferous, which is mainly composed of massive limestones deposited in a shallow warm sea, and the Upper Carboniferous containing most of the coal that has been worked in Britain, which was deposited on swampy plains on the fringe of a continent.

However, in South-west England a different scenario was unfolding, and the sediments of Carboniferous age were wholly deposited in an east-west marine basin. In what is now northern Cornwall and mid Devon the sea became markedly deeper at the beginning of the Carboniferous, and this seems to represent a deep trench which developed in front of the newly emerging mountains of the Variscan fold-belt further south. In this trench at first there was slow sedimentation, with cherts and dark shales and some volcanicity. Later on great quantities of mud and sand began to enter the trough, perhaps resulting in part from the erosion of the mountains rising to the south. Much of this sediment was emplaced by turbidity currents, and turbidite deposits are well shown in the cliffs from Boscastle north to the Devon border.

No Carboniferous sediments are found in south and west Cornwall, in spite of there being an almost complete sequence of Devonian strata. Although we cannot be sure that they were never deposited, this absolute lack of Carboniferous sediments suggests that deformation and uplift south of the Start-Perranporth Line (SPL) had started in earnest by the Early Carboniferous. Many of the major fold and thrust structures, such as the Carrick Thrust, had probably already been formed before the end of the Devonian Period.

The indications are that the Early Carboniferous mountain-building died out quite rapidly north of the SPL, although we must remember that north-south distances have been greatly reduced by later thrust faulting. The Lower Carboniferous from Tintagel eastwards through Launceston and on towards Exeter was deposited in deep water, so the submarine slope on the northern side of the early Variscan mountains must have been steep. Indeed, it was sufficiently steep in the later part of the Early Carboniferous to cause huge sheets of Late Devonian and Early Carboniferous sediments and their associated igneous rocks to slide off the rising land-mass to the south, under gravity, into deep water in the Launceston area.

Besides these gravity-driven sheets, there are also later true thrust faults resulting from compression. There is a tendency in the geological literature for the slide surfaces at the base of gravity-driven slump sheets to be called thrust faults, and it has to be admitted that the two are very difficult to distinguish in the field.

South-east Cornwall is complicated by a zone of major dextral strike-slip faults called the **Plymouth-Cambeak Fault Zone**, which have cumulatively resulted in

Cornwall being shifted northwards by about 20-30 km in relation to Devon (see *Figures 5* and *57*). This fault zone, with several fault planes, intersects the north coast between Rusey Beach and just north of Cambeak, between 2 and 3 miles northeast of Boscastle. Strangely, the dextral movement on the north coast, where it affects Carboniferous rocks only, appears to be much less than in the area southeast of Bodmin Moor, where only Devonian rocks are involved. One explanation might be that the main movement on the Plymouth-Cambeak Fault Zone took place in the first phase of mountain building in the Early Carboniferous, with the Upper Carboniferous sediments from Boscastle northwards being deposited after the main phase of movement.

The Rusey Fault (*Figures 5* and *53*) is clearly an important boundary, with Upper Carboniferous rocks only to the north of it, and mainly Lower Carboniferous rocks to the south. For convenience, we will start by describing the rocks to the south of the Rusey Fault, working from west to east. The sequence of Carboniferous rocks in different parts of Cornwall is indicated in *Figure 48* and the palaeogeography in *Figure 50*.

South of the Rusey Fault

In the **Tintagel area** we are in the **Tredorn Nappe** (see p 51). A number of low-angle faults (some authors call them thrust faults) have long been recognised (see *Figure 32* and *Figure 33*), which results in a stack of nappes with the same sequence being repeated in each:

Lower Carboniferous	Trambley Cove Formation
	Tintagel Volcanic Formation
	Barras Nose Formation
	Transition Group – grey slates
Upper Devonian	Tredorn Slates, etc.

Between the Devonian Tredorn Slates and the Carboniferous Barras Nose Formation there are some grey slates known as the **Transition Group**, which probably span the Devonian/Carboniferous boundary. Trilobites (*Cyrtosymbole*) belonging to the lower-most Carboniferous have been found in Transition Group slates in California Quarry (on the coast due west of Boscastle) but, apart from the ubiquitous crinoid ossicles, there is little other fossil material.

The **Barras Nose Formation** consists of dark grey and black slates, with occasional bands of volcanic rocks such as ash and lava, and some limestones. It is seen in the narrow isthmus joining Tintagel Island to the mainland and at Barras Nose itself (see *Figure 33*). The limestones have yielded conodonts which indicate the age to be the middle of the Lower Carboniferous (the Tournaisian/Viséan boundary – see *Figure 48*). The darker colour of the slates indicates a high carbon content, caused by organic material falling on the sea bottom failing to decompose due a lack of oxygen (*anoxic conditions*). This condition is usually associated with deep basins that have a sluggish or non-existent water circulation.

The **Tintagel Volcanic Formation** outcrops widely in the Tintagel area and is probably best seen at Trebarwith Strand. These volcanic rocks have been subjected to greater strain and higher temperatures than the volcanics in the Padstow area and hence

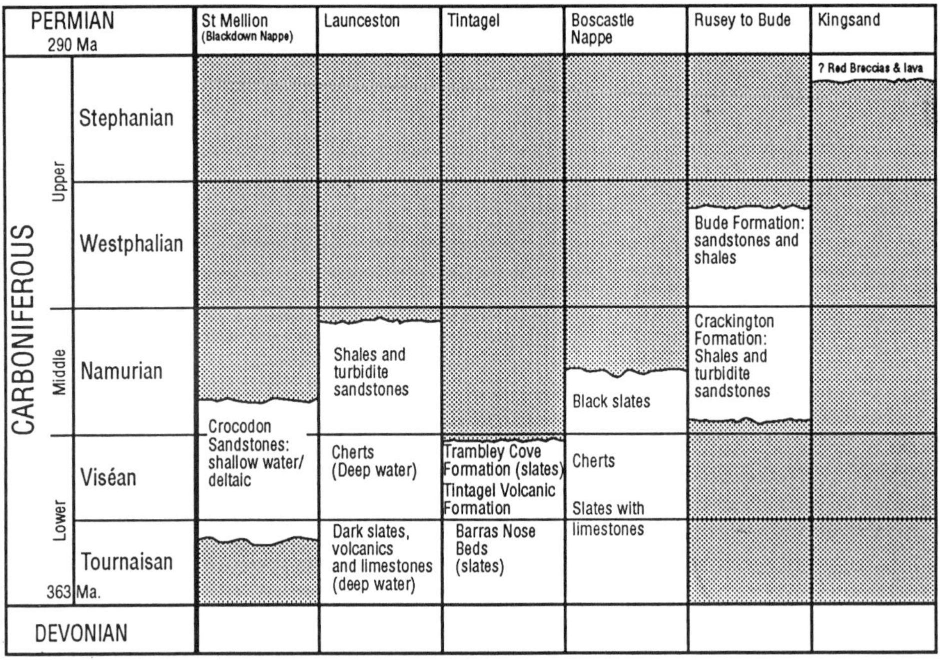

PERMIAN 290 Ma	St Mellion (Blackdown Nappe)	Launceston	Tintagel	Boscastle Nappe	Rusey to Bude	Kingsand
						? Red Breccias & lava
Upper — Stephanian						
Upper — Westphalian					Bude Formation: sandstones and shales	
Middle — Namurian		Shales and turbidite sandstones		Black slates	Crackington Formation: Shales and turbidite sandstones	
Lower — Viséan	Crocodon Sandstones: shallow water/ deltaic	Cherts (Deep water)	Trambley Cove Formation (slates) / Tintagel Volcanic Formation	Cherts		
Lower — Tournaisan 363 Ma.		Dark slates, volcanics and limestones (deep water)	Barras Nose Beds (slates)	Slates with limestones		
DEVONIAN						

(Left margin spanning labels: CARBONIFEROUS; Upper / Middle / Lower)

Figure 48 *The sequences of Carboniferous rocks to be found in Cornwall. The stages (subdivisions of geological periods) are given on the left hand side.*

have been metamorphosed to 'greenschist' level, which has resulted in new minerals forming in the rock such as albite, chlorite, epidote and biotite. Many complicated structural explanations have been offered to account for this area of unusually intense metamorphism, one of the simplest being to interpret it as some rocks brought up from a deeper level by uplift on the west side of the Plymouth-Cambeak Fault Zone.

At Trebarwith Strand, lenses of basic lava are set in an intensely sheared matrix. The lenses may represent the remains of the cores of pillows and the matrix the sheared softer material between the pillows. The Tintagel Volcanic Formation can be traced as far east as Lewannick, northeast of Bodmin Moor. Pillow lavas seen on both sides of the River Inny near St Clether may possibly belong to the eastward continuation of this formation.

Above it comes the **Trambley Cove Formation**, which is another sequence of grey and black slates, poorly fossiliferous and with occasional bands of volcanic tuff and siltstone.

Once north of Boscastle we find the geology has changed again and we are in the **Boscastle Nappe**, which contains a quite different sequence of Carboniferous rocks, with the volcanic sequence seen to the north between Trebarwith and Boscastle not represented at all. This is an extremely complex area (*Figure 49*), and difficult to interpret. There is isoclinal folding and much evidence of repetition by low-angle faulting, as well as NW-SE strike-slip faulting. Much of the coastal section appears to consist of Namurian black slates (dated by means of goniatites such as *Homoceras* and *Reticuloceras*), green slates and limestones of Tournaisian/Viséan age (*Figure 48*); and Lower Carboniferous cherts, known as the **Fire Beacon Chert Formation**, seem to

76

Figure 49 *Folded black siltstones and slates of mid-Carboniferous age at Boscastle (lens cap shows the scale).*

have been introduced by faulting into this predominantly Namurian sequence.

In the **Launceston** area the situation is again complicated by the extent of the faulting and we seem to be dealing with a stack of slump sheets which have been cut up by later thrust faulting and strike-slip faulting (see page 54). Unfortunately the exposures of the rocks in this area are poor, making the structural interpretation difficult.

Some of the earliest slump sheets were emplaced late in the Lower Carboniferous, and they probably represent sheets of sediment which slid off the rising areas to the west and south soon after they had been deposited. These sheets then glided down into the deep water on the northern side of the emerging mountain chain (*Figure 51*). Such a development bears some resemblance to the foundering of large areas of sediment, including the Ordovician quartzites, that led to the development of the Roseland Breccia, so this could be another example of an olistostrome.

Later nappes may have involved true deep-seated thrusts driven by pressure from the south. There appears to be a 'Basement Unit', on top of which all the other nappes have been placed; this is named the 'Kate Brook Unit', after a locality near Chudleigh in Devon, where it was first recognised in the 1960s. It is best seen across the Devon border in Lydford Gorge, where it shows higher levels of metamorphism than the overlying nappes.

Higher nappes give a very confused picture of the stratigraphy. The sequence everywhere seems to start with a Transition Group of slates, comparable to that seen at Tintagel, which were probably laid down in deep water. We then see a wide variety of

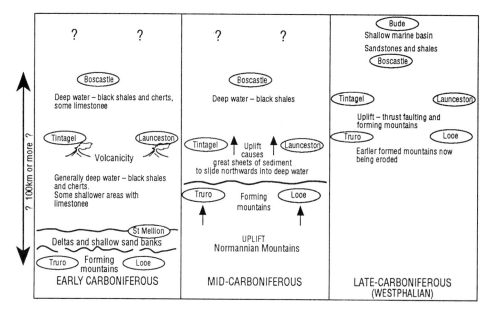

Figure 50 *Series of sketch maps to indicate the approximate disposition of land and sea, etc. at various times during the Carboniferous Period. Note that there was extensive north-south shortening in the Variscan Orogeny, due to thrust faults telescoping the sedimentary sequences.*

environments developed in the later part of the Lower Carboniferous. Thick sequences of dark-coloured slates with few fossils are frequently found, probably representing a basinal situation where there is a constant drizzle of mud settling out on a sea bottom, which is barren of life because of a lack of oxygen in the water (*anoxic*). Slates of this type are seen in the road cutting on the Launceston by-pass (A30) between the town and the Tamar. Dark-grey and black Carboniferous slates were formerly extensively quarried in the Launceston area and widely used for local building, particularly in Launceston, although the slate was said not to weather as well as Delabole slate.

In some of the nappes we find radiolarian cherts and shales which would seem to indicate deep-basin conditions where the supply of sediment from the land was minimal. Radiolarian cherts are a common feature of the Lower Carboniferous in the Launceston area and also in north and south Devon. They are hard, dark-grey, flinty rocks, composed of almost pure silica, with individual beds about 10 cm thick. The beds are usually separated by soft, pale-coloured shaly partings which result in the bedding being unusually prominent. Provided they are not too strongly recrystallised, one can usually make out minute white specks with a hand lens which, under the microscope, turn out to be the siliceous skeletons of single-celled organisms known as radiolaria, although rarely sufficiently well preserved for their genus to be identified.

In the present-day oceans radiolarian oozes are found at abyssal depths, below the carbonate-compensation level (the depth below which calcium carbonate is dissolved back into the sea water). In the present day Pacific Ocean, this level is at a depth of 4500 m and there is no reason to believe that it would have been greatly different in the equatorial seas of the Carboniferous. Occasional thin limestones associated with the

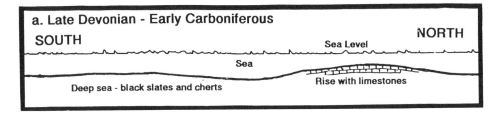

a. Late Devonian - Early Carboniferous

SOUTH

NORTH

Sea Level

Sea

Deep sea - black slates and cherts

Rise with limestones

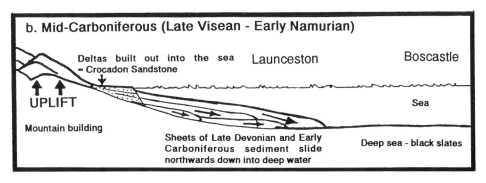

b. Mid-Carboniferous (Late Visean - Early Namurian)

Deltas built out into the sea = Crocadon Sandstone

Launceston

Boscastle

UPLIFT

Sea

Mountain building

Sheets of Late Devonian and Early Carboniferous sediment slide northwards down into deep water

Deep sea - black slates

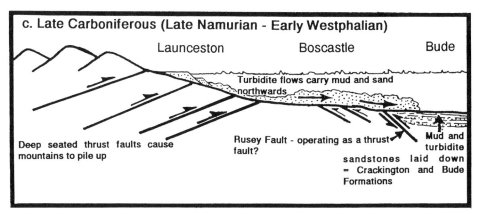

c. Late Carboniferous (Late Namurian - Early Westphalian)

Launceston

Boscastle

Bude

Turbidite flows carry mud and sand northwards

Deep seated thrust faults cause mountains to pile up

Rusey Fault - operating as a thrust fault?

Mud and turbidite sandstones laid down = Crackington and Bude Formations

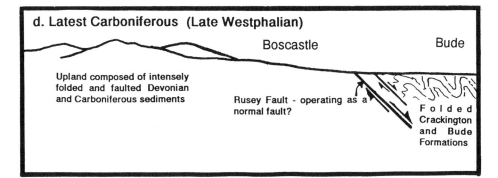

d. Latest Carboniferous (Late Westphalian)

Boscastle

Bude

Upland composed of intensely folded and faulted Devonian and Carboniferous sediments

Rusey Fault - operating as a normal fault?

Folded Crackington and Bude Formations

Figure 51 *Conjectural sequence of events in north Cornwall during the Carboniferous Period.*

cherts of the Launceston area suggest that the Carboniferous sea was sometimes just above the carbonate-compensation depth. The combination of radiolarian cherts, black slates and spilitic (sodium-rich) pillow lavas is frequently found in the geological record and almost invariably means that the beds were deposited in deep water, usually in an active tectonic zone.

In other nappes in the Launceston area we find limestones and sandstones, which indicate shallower conditions, perhaps in the form of a submarine rise, or as shallower water fringing the land-mass to the south or west. The limestones have yielded many macrofossils such as goniatites, trilobites and brachiopods, and microfossils such as conodonts, which can be used for dating and correlation.

The thickness of the chert and limestone sequences in the Lower Carboniferous is not known for certain, but is probably not much more than 100 m. This implies a very slow rate of sedimentation, for further north in the Mendip Hills the Lower Carboniferous can attain a thickness of over 700 m.

Yet another environment is represented by turbiditic sandstones and shales (the Cotehele Formation), perhaps originating from deltas built out into the sea by rivers draining the emerging mountains to the south and west. This last type of sediment is found as early as the latest Devonian, which suggests the emergence of the southern land-mass (which we have been calling 'Normannia' in the previous chapter) started before the end of the Devonian.

Further south, underlying the high ground between Callington and St Mellion, a nappe containing a thick group of sandstones, siltstones and shales is found, known as the **Crocadon Sandstone**. The feldspathic sandstones appear to have been derived from the rapid erosion of a wide range of crystalline and sedimentary rocks, including Devonian and perhaps Early Carboniferous rocks. They show the characteristics of having been laid down in shallow water and contain much land-derived plant material. A few horizons which represent old land surfaces have been found, sometimes with the roots of land plants preserved. These indicate that the sediments were probably deposited on the outer fringes of a delta, built out by a river draining the northern slopes of the emerging mountains to the south and west. However, sedimentary structures (grading, sole marks) indicate that the whole sequence is upside down and the source of the slump sheet or nappe containing these sediments is unknown, so it is difficult to attempt any form of meaningful palaeogeographic reconstruction. A few goniatites have been found in some of the marine beds interbedded with the sandstones, and these, together with spores, suggest that the whole of the Crocadon Sandstone is of Early Carboniferous age.

Volcanism is well represented in the Lower Carboniferous of the Launceston area and extends over the Devon border into the Tavistock area. There is little evidence of volcanicity in the foundation Kate Brook Unit (autochthon) but, in the overlying stack of nappes, lavas and tuffs are well represented, as well as intrusive sills, presumed to be part of the same phase of igneous activity, which commenced in the latest Tournaisian and was completed by the end of the Viséan. Nearly all the volcanic material is basic in character, and some is ultrabasic. Pillow lavas are seen in places and it is likely that the volcanicity was wholly submarine.

Intrusive dolerite sills are superbly displayed in Greystone Quarry, a few miles southeast of Launceston. This quarry has been extremely busy in recent years, providing the material needed to upgrade the A30 to dual carriageway, so there are

Figure 52 *The chilled contact of a Carboniferous dolerite intrusion at Greystone Quarry, near Launceston. The lighter-coloured dolerite below has a sharp horizontal boundary with the darker siliceous slate above, in which carbonate mineral veins (calcite) can be seen.*

currently plenty of fresh faces. The uppermost bench shows Upper Devonian slate, which has been superimposed on the dolerite by a low-angle fault (the Greystone 'thrust'– see *Figure 11d*); this may be the bottom of a slump sheet which arrived in place under gravity. The dolerite is generally fine grained and there are two sheets, separated by some siliceous shales which have been baked by the heat of the intrusions to become chert-like rocks. The bedding in these dark shales is clearly visible and the chilled contact at the edge of the intrusion is seen in the lowest bench of the quarry (*Figure 52*). An east-west lead/silver lode crosses the southwestern corner of the quarry and has normal fault movement associated with it (*Figure 11a*).

An even more exotic rock type is found at Polyphant, where ultrabasic rocks and gabbros are found, not unlike some of the rocks in the Lizard Complex. The ultrabasic rock has traditionally been called a picrite; when fresh, it is mainly composed of the mineral olivine. The intrusion is probably bounded by low-angle faults above and below, so it is detached from the original environment into which it was intruded. Parts of this ultrabasic mass have suffered an interesting form of alteration where water charged with carbon dioxide has passed through the rock and altered it to a mixture of talc and various forms of Ca/Mg/Fe carbonate. This soft rock is 'Polyphant stone', which has been widely used since medieval times for buildings, principally for interior work. The quarry lies to the north of the village, and was worked until the 1950s; it was recently reopened to provide stone for the restoration of Newquay parish church.

Studies of the chemistry of the basic volcanics in the Launceston area show they have MORB affinities. This may indicate that, in the earlier part of the Lower

Figure 53 *The Rusey Fault as seen at the base of the cliffs at Rusey Beach, 2.5 miles northeast of Boscastle. The mass of quartz in the main fault zone can be seen dipping at about 45° to the north (left-hand side of figure). Boulders at the bottom of the face are about one foot in diameter.*

Carboniferous, there was a brief period of crustal tension which led to the incipient development of the kind of igneous activity associated with oceanic spreading axes.

The band of country to the north of Launceston, between the presumed inland extension of the Rusey Fault and the northernmost boundary of the Upper Devonian (see *Figure 5* is the eastward continuation of the Boscastle Nappe. It is mainly occupied by black slates with occasional beds of turbidite sandstone. These appear to be mainly of Namurian age, although some lenses of Tournaisian and Viséan rocks have somehow been structurally incorporated into this complex unit. Slates and turbiditic sandstones with small-scale fold structures are visible in a road cutting at Newport, north of Launceston, where the B3254 branches off from the A388.

North of the Rusey Fault

Rusey Beach is about two miles northeast of Boscastle and it marks yet another major change in the geology. By coincidence, two important faults reach the coast at this point so, as ever with Cornish geology, the interpretation is not straightforward. The main fault is a low-angle east-west fault dipping northwards, known as the Rusey Fault *(Figure 53)*, and the other is a NW-SE dextral strike-slip fault which is part of the Plymouth-Cambeak Fault Zone.

At Rusey Beach the core of the main Rusey Fault is seen to be occupied by a thick mass of quartz dipping northwards at about 45°. The quartz is intensely sheared, as are the slates on either side. Some barely recognisable shreds of Lower Carboniferous chert

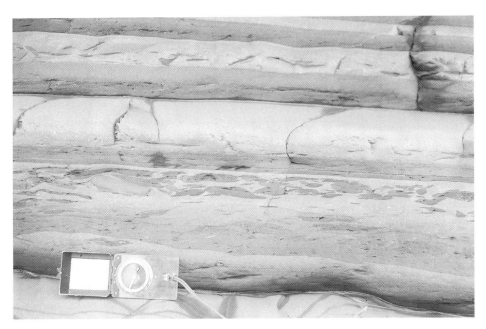

Figure 54 Graded bedding and turbidite units of Late Carboniferous age in the area north of the Rusey Fault. Pellets of shale have been torn up by the turbidity current and incorporated into some of the sandstones.

Figure 55 An angular recumbent fold in Late Carboniferous turbidite sandstones and shales at Millook Haven, 2 miles southwest of Widemouth.

and limestone are also seen in the fault zone and it is clear we are dealing with a fault of unusual significance. The metamorphic grade of the rocks to the south of the fault is higher, suggesting a vertical displacement of several kilometres. One explanation could be that the fault acted as a thrust during the earlier part of the Carboniferous, which reversed at a later date, becoming a normal fault (see *Figure 51*).

The NW-SE strike-slip fault at Rusey is part of a whole series of dextral (offsetting to the right) strike-slip faults which reach the coast between Rusey Beach, Cambeak and St Gennys. They are part of the Plymouth-Cambeak Fault Zone and, although they displace the Rusey Fault, it is not by a great amount, and certainly not the 20 km or so of combined dextral movement seen on the same fault system in southeast Cornwall.

Whatever the nature of the faults at Rusey Beach, we find that the geology to the north is distinctly different and we are dealing exclusively with rocks belonging to the Namurian and Westphalian Stages of the Upper Carboniferous (*Figure 48*).

The formation exposed on the coast between Rusey Beach and Widemouth is known as the **Crackington Formation**. On the coast this formation is seen to be composed of a sequence of dark slaty shales alternating with sandstones. The latter are clearly turbiditic in character as they demonstrate the graded bedding and sole markings (flute casts, load casts, groove casts etc.), typical of sediments laid down by turbidity currents. The erosion of the mountains to the south was feeding vast quantities of muddy sediment, via the rivers draining their northern slopes and a series of deltas, into the marine trough to the north.

On the northern side of the trough, the rivers flowing through the coal swamps of South Wales and the Bristol area were building out a fringe of deltas. Periodic storms, or earth movements, caused the unstable delta-fronts to collapse, producing a high-density slurry which rushed downslope to the floor of the trough; here the sediment settled out, coarse sandy grains first, followed by the finer clayey fraction (*Figure 54*). The movement of the high-density slurry across the floor of the sea scooped out small hollows in the sea floor, known as **flute casts**. As the soft sandy bed was consolidating and losing its high initial water content, it tended to form lobes which protruded down into the soft sediment underneath, and these are known as **load casts.**

Goniatites such as *Reticuloceras* and *Homoceras* indicate that most of the Crackington Formation is Namurian in age.

The most striking feature with these rocks is the folding. The bold alternation between dark shales and pale sandstones makes the folds stand out clearly One of the most striking locations to see this is at Millook Haven, where a cascade of sharp-angled folds is seen in the cliff (*Figure 55*). These folds have horizontal axial planes (they are lying on their sides, i.e. are recumbent) and were probably formed not long after the sediments were deposited, at some time in the late Westphalian.

The **Bude Formation** occupies the coast from Widemouth up to the Devon border. It typically has thick sandstone beds, non-graded, suggestive of a non-turbidite origin, with siltstones and dark shales. Some of the sandstones have fine flute casts underneath (*Figure 56*), so some of the sandstone bodies were formed by turbidites. Goniatites such as *Gastrioceras* indicate a Westphalian age. The environment was still marine, but we are now dealing with the final act in the infilling of the trough that started off life as the Rheic Ocean. On many slabs tracks of king-crabs (xiphosurans) can be seen, and fossil xiphosurans have also been found; detailed studies of the tracks in the Bude area have shown that the habits of the Westphalian xiphosurans were

Figure 56 *Sole (underside) markings on the base of a Late Carboniferous turbidite sandstone south of Bude. These features can be used to determine the direction of the turbidity current; most seem to indicate that the currents flowed along the axis of the supposed east-west trough.*

basically the same as the modern king-crab. Slump beds are found in the coastal section south of Bude, which indicate tectonic instability in the area, no doubt related to the mountain building which was going on not far to the south. Some fine text-book examples of anticlines and synclines are seen in the shales and sandstones south of Bude (*Front Cover, Figures 8a* and *8b*); note that these folds have vertical axial planes and are not recumbent.

Further north in the Bideford area, there are sediments similar in age to the Bude Formation, but they do have true coal seams, which were exploited in the past for a form of anthracite known as 'culm'; hence the term 'Culm Measures', which is used to describe the Carboniferous rocks of Devon and Cornwall in the older literature. The culm seams indicate that the great coal swamps of the Westphalian did extend as far south as Devon in the final stages of the infilling of the trough.

This brings to an end our journey in time through the period when the Devonian and Carboniferous sediments were being laid down in Cornwall; the Variscan Orogeny now engulfs the whole area and the marine trough is eliminated. This will be the subject of the next chapter.

7 *The Variscan mountain-building episode*

As the mountains and islands of Normannia, forming the leading edge of the tectonic plate carrying most of France in the Devonian, moved slowly and inexorably northwards, it crunched into the south side of the Old Red Sandstone continent, with the result that huge masses of crust rode over one another and the layered sedimentary rocks were contorted and buckled into folds of all sizes. As the pile of deformed rocks in the collision zone grew, it formed a mountain range. This cataclysmic tectonic event is known to geologists as the **Variscan Orogeny**.

Because much of the structural history has already been dealt with in the last three chapters, the following is a synthesis of what happened in the orogeny.

Timing of the orogenic events

As we have seen, the gathering storm of the Variscan Orogeny began in the south of the area as early as the Middle Devonian (about 380 Ma), but did not affect the Carboniferous sediments around Bude until the later part of the Westphalian Stage of the Late Carboniferous (about 310 Ma). Still further north, in the Somerset coalfield, we find that the whole of the Westphalian is present, and perhaps some of the still-later Stephanian Stage as well, so the main period of deformation there was probably as late as 300 Ma. So, the orogeny rumbled on for around 80 million years from the first perceptible stirrings in the south of Cornwall to the final phase of deformation in Somerset.

However, the orogeny does not seem to have made a steady progression from south to north. There appear to have been two major pulses of compression, and there is some evidence to suggest that these were separated by a period of extension in the later part of the Early Carboniferous.

An oblique collision

The collision between the tectonic plates appears to have been oblique, with the French plate moving in a northwesterly direction, pushing Cornwall north and west. *Figure 57* shows how the northwestward shunt of Cornwall was accommodated by movement along the transform Plymouth-Cambeak Fault Zone. The parallel but smaller Tamar Valley Fault Zone also may have functioned in a similar way. **Transform faults** are really strike-slip faults, but on a grander scale. They are characteristic features of plate tectonics – the classic example is the San Andreas fault in California. Further east, in northern France and crossing the channel to southern England, another major transform fault known as the 'Bray Fault' ran parallel to the Plymouth-Cambeak Fault Zone and performed a similar function, allowing the region to the west of it also to be shunted northwestwards.

The ancient line of weakness represented by the Start-Perranporth Line, although oblique to the sense of movement of the plates, probably also accommodated some dextral movement along its length during the initial pulse of the Variscan Orogeny in

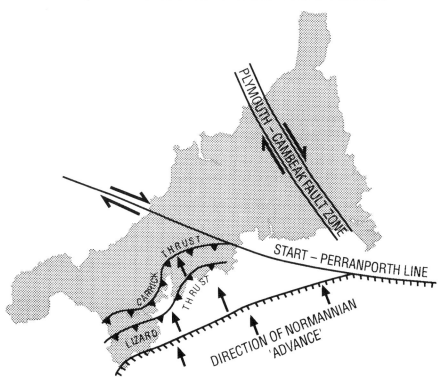

Figure 57 *Diagram to illustrate the fault zone along which Cornwall was shunted northwards in relation to Devon during the early stage of the Variscan Orogeny. The break that allowed this northwards movement was the Plymouth-Cambeak Fault Zone, the position of which is indicated in the diagram.*

the Early Carboniferous, allowing Cornwall south of the SPL to move westwards in relation to the area to the north.

The early phase of the orogeny

The earliest indication of the orogeny is detected in the Roseland area of southern Cornwall by the incoming of coarse sediments in the Middle Devonian (about 380 Ma) representing debris derived from the erosion of the rising land of Normannia. Major deep-seated thrusts, possibly related to a southward-dipping subduction zone off the south coast of Cornwall, allowed the sea floor to be steadily telescoped by movement on this stack of thrusts. Some oceanic crust, formed in the Frasnian Stage of the Devonian, was caught up in the thrust movements and came to form some slices between sedimentary rocks of Devonian age, so creating the Lizard ophiolite. As the oceanic crust had only just been formed at the time the thrust movements started, it was still hot, which explains why high-grade metamorphic rocks are found in the Lizard complex.

The northernmost thrust fault associated with the northward movement of the Normannian mass is the Carrick Thrust, which runs under Truro (see *Figure 57*). The eastern end of the Carrick Thrust looks from the map as if its movement has been taken up by dextral strike-slip movement on the Start-Perranporth Line. However, the earlier views of Hendriks that the Roseland area was formed from *gravity-driven* nappes should not be forgotten, as this accords well with the major slumping represented by the Roseland Breccia Formation. Gravity-driven nappes could represent the earliest phase of the orogenic deformation, and the nappe above the Carrick Thrust Fault may also have been gravity-driven (*Figure 36 b,c*).

Folding in this first phase of the Variscan Orogeny mainly took the form of recumbent isoclinal folds, facing northwards. There are many fine examples of this type of folding to be seen in south and west Cornwall (*Figure 8d*). This style of folding continues northwards as far as the Padstow Confrontation.

The oldest Devonian rocks – the Dartmouth Group of Early Devonian age – are brought up by a combination of faulting and folding in a zone extending from Watergate Bay in the west through to southeast Cornwall. This structure continues eastwards into south Devon and is known as the Dartmouth antiform.

The area between the Padstow Confrontation and the Rusey Fault is very complex and it may well be that we are looking at the combined effects of two orogenic pulses in this area. Early upright folding may belong to the earlier phase, but the dominant sense of movement seems to be towards the south and therefore probably belongs to the Late Carboniferous phase of the orogeny. There has been a great deal of controversy over which way the low-angle faults in the Tintagel area moved; perhaps they moved in different directions at different times. They could even represent sheets of sediment sliding off a rising area, perhaps in the vicinity of Bodmin Moor.

In the Launceston area there is some evidence that there was a brief period of crustal stretching in the later part of the Early Carboniferous, which led to volcanicity with MORB (= Mid Ocean Ridge Basalt) affinities. This could have been after the first pulse of the orogeny in the earlier part of the Early Carboniferous, but before the second pulse in the Late Carboniferous. It is possible that crustal stretching was happening in the Launceston area, at the same time as mountains were being raised further south.

The later phase of the orogeny

There is evidence from the Launceston-St Mellion area that, by the end of Early Carboniferous times, areas of sea floor to the west and south were being elevated sufficiently rapidly that they were becoming unstable, shedding great sheets of semi-consolidated sediment which slid down into the deeper waters to the north and east to form a jumble of sheets, one on top of another (*Figure 51*). Some of the sediments involved had been deposited after the first phase of the orogeny in the Early Carboniferous, for example the Crocodon Sandstone of the St Mellion area. Later, true orogenic thrust faults, belonging to the Late Carboniferous phase of the orogeny, cut through this jumble of sheets, making it incredibly difficult to unravel the structure.

In the main Culm trough north of the Rusey Fault there are only Upper Carboniferous sediments, so the Early Carboniferous earth movements cannot have affected these rocks. Sedimentation ceased, as far as we know, at about 310-305 Ma, towards the end of the Westphalian Stage of the Carboniferous.

Simple north-south compression appears to have produced most of the structures we see from Rusey up to the Devon border. Many of the Late Carboniferous upright folds in the Bude area and further north are on a sufficiently small scale to be seen in the cliffs (*Figures 8a* and *8b*). However, the cascade of zig-zag folds at Millook (*Figure 55*) suggests an overriding movement towards the north, and many geologists believe that this whole mass of Carboniferous sediments has slid northwards on a major very-low-angle fault at depth. A normal phase of movement on the northward-dipping 45° fault plane of the Rusey Fault could be part of this northwards 'slide'.

The enigma of the Rusey Fault

The Rusey Fault (*Figures 51* and *53*) is a major element in the structure which became active in the Late Carboniferous (as far as we know, for it may have an earlier history for which we have no evidence). Whilst many syntheses of the structure of north Cornwall mark the Rusey Fault as acting as a thrust during the initial stages of the Variscan Orogeny, in fact it looks as if it acted as a normal fault at a later stage, for the rocks in the hanging wall (the northern side) are much lower in metamorphic grade, suggesting that the northern side has been downthrown several kilometres. One interpretation suggests that the later Carboniferous sediments of north Cornwall and central Devon are in an east-west fault trough, with the southern side formed by the Rusey Fault and the northern side formed by an east-west fault through Barnstaple. If the area south of the Rusey Fault was upthrown, then slabs of sediment sliding down the 45° ramp of the Rusey Fault could have pushed against the sediments to the north and contributed towards their folding.

Strike-slip faults – the 'cross-courses'

Strike-slip faults involve horizontal movement of one block of ground past an adjoining block (*Figure 10d*). They are generally approximately vertical. Strike-slip faults, usually aligned N-S or NW-SE, were called by the old miners 'cross-courses'. There appears to have been an important phase of movement along these faults at a late stage in the Variscan Orogeny, just before the intrusion of the granites, although movement along these lines of weakness may have taken place earlier, and certainly has taken place on several occasions since the intrusion of the granites.

Two major strike-slip fault zones have already been mentioned. Firstly, there is the Start-Perranporth Line (SPL), which traverses Cornwall from Holywell Bay/Perran Bay to Mevagissey/St Austell Bay and which appears to have moved in a dextral sense in Devonian times. The SPL is actually aligned almost east-west and probably owes its origins to an ancient line of weakness in the underlying crust, so it is not really part of the more general NW-SE or N-S strike-slip faulting seen in the county. Secondly, the Plymouth-Cambeak Fault Zone is composed of the Cawsand and Portwrinkle Faults west of Plymouth and intersects the north coast in the Rusey-Cambeak stretch of coast (*Figure 57*). As was mentioned earlier, the movement on this fault where it affects Devonian sediments in the south is a great deal more than where it affects the Carboniferous sediments on the north coast; this may indicate that the main phase of movement on this fault was pre-mid-Carboniferous.

There is a great deal of strike-slip faulting in the area between the Devon border and the Bodmin Moor granite, with two zones of concentrated movement: the Plymouth-Cambeak Fault Zone already mentioned and the Tamar Valley Fault Zone (TVFZ). The Palaeogene (early Tertiary) Dutson Basin just east of Launceston (see Chapter 11) lies on the TVFZ and must represent a rejuvenation of the faults of the TVFZ much later in the Palaeogene Period. Further south, faults belonging to the TVFZ clip the Hingston Down granite on both sides, and the River Tamar has cut its valley along the line of weakness represented by the TVFZ.

MOUNTAINS AT THE HEIGHT OF THE OROGENY: Compression as the tectonic plates collide causes high mountains to pile up; the resulting accumulation of less-dense continental crust up to 40 km thick sags down into the denser mantle to form the 'root' under the mountain range

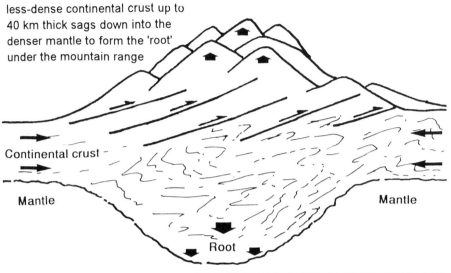

POST-OROGENIC COLLAPSE: Once the plate collision ceases, the forces of compression sustaining the mountains are removed, and they begin to collapse under their own weight. As the mountains are eroded, the buoyancy of the root forces the mountains up, so gravitational collapse is prolonged

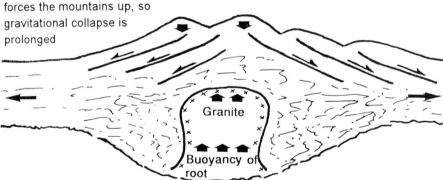

The process is accentuated if a granite mass starts to rise up through the core of a mountain range

Figure 58   *Diagram to illustrate how the high mountains created during the Variscan Orogeny subsequently collapsed – a process known as 'post-orogenic gravitational collapse'.*

Further west in Cornwall, there are many further strike-slip faults aligned NW-SE or N-S, nearly all with a dextral sense of movement. Many, such as the Fal Valley Fault (see *Figure 63*), are demonstrably pre-granite in age, whilst others such as the Great Cross-Course on Par Moor had a significant phase of movement after the mineral veins had been formed. Some of this movement may have been as late as the Palaeogene, when compressive stresses again affected South-west England due to the effects of the formation of the Alps far away to the south. Although these faults were probably initiated during the Variscan Orogeny, it is often difficult to separate the extent of the pre-granite movement from the post-granite and post-mineralisation movement. The rocks in the strike-slip fault zones are normally altered and soft, so these faults often cause prominent indentations in the coastline.

The collapse of the Variscan mountain chain

At the end of the main compressive phase of the Variscan Orogeny, South-west England formed part of a mighty mountain chain known as the Variscides, stretching from Poland to southern Ireland. Crumpled rocks formed the mountain range and, because of the force of the collision, the crust under the mountain range had been abnormally thickened, perhaps up to 40 km in places.

However, that was not the end of the tectonic activity, for the compression of the Variscan Orogeny was followed by a relaxation of pressure, with a kind of 'rebound' situation. As soon as the compressive forces were relaxed the high mountains became unstable and began to collapse – a process known as 'post-orogenic gravitational collapse' (*Figure 58*). This caused extensional WSW-ENE normal faults to develop. Faults of this type are common around St Agnes and affect the mineral lodes (Wheal Kitty and Penhalls mines); some small-scale faults from this area are shown in *Figure 11b*. These faults are also seen on the north coast, perhaps most notably in the cliffs near Portreath, where low-angle normal faults dipping seaward produce lines of weakness along which failure frequently occurs, in the upper cliff.

The normal faults which define the northern boundary of the Lizard Complex probably belong to this phase of extensional movement (see *Figure 47*, page 70-71). At the Polurrian (western) end of the Lizard boundary, the fault dips towards the southeast at 45° and at the Porthallow (eastern) side it dips at the same angle, but to the south. The low-angle features (see *Figure 47*) identified on seismic geophysical surveys of the seabed south of Cornwall have hitherto been identified as thrust faults, but could have been reactivated to become low-angle normal faults during the period of extension we are talking about.

As we will see in the next chapter, the granites were generated and intruded towards the end of the compressive phase and during the early stages of gravitational collapse; and the high temperature metalliferous mineralisation took place mainly in the phase of extension and normal faulting that followed.

8 *The intrusion of the granites into the heart of the Variscan mountains*

Most of the high ground of Cornwall and Devon, with the exception of Exmoor, is underlain by granite, either at the surface or at a depth of a few kilometres. This is no coincidence, for not only is granite relatively resistant to erosion, it is also slightly less dense than the surrounding rocks, so it tends to buoy up the peninsula – a process geologists call *isostatic uplift*. Without the granites, most of Cornwall would probably be below the waters of the Atlantic Ocean. Precise measurements of the strength of the earth's gravitational field show lower values over the granites because of their lower density, from which the shape of the underlying granite mass can be calculated, showing that deep below the peninsula the different granites appear to merge into one great mass, known as a **batholith**, which underlies over half of the Cornish land-mass.

Our ideas concerning the origin of the granites have undergone considerable revision over the last few years, mainly because new and more accurate methods of dating have become available. We used to think that the whole granite batholith was intruded at more or less the same time, but we now believe that each of the granite masses was separately generated and intruded at different times over a period of 30 million years, so the earliest ones were cooling and being mineralised before the intrusion of the latest granites had commenced.

Origin of the granites

The simplest way to envisage the origin of the Cornish granites is to imagine melting a large mass of sedimentary rocks such as slate and sandstone, and then allowing the resulting melt to cool very slowly. Careful research into the geochemistry of our granites suggests that, although they may have partly originated from the melting of Devonian or Carboniferous rocks, it is more likely that they were mainly derived from the melting of older metamorphic rocks, lying at depth beneath the younger Devonian and Carboniferous cover.

Sometimes a whole mass of sedimentary rocks was so highly metamorphosed that it melted in place, preserving as ghost-like features some traces of the original sedimentary layers. These are known as **migmatites** and are common in Brittany. In other situations the molten granite rises up through the crust to form a **magmatic** or **intrusive granite**. The granites of South-west England are of this type and have definitely originated by melting at depth and subsequent migration by flow to intrude the upper part of the crust.

However, a puzzle remains as to how and why the granites were generated to begin with. One of the most popular explanations is that, during the collision of the two tectonic plates during the Variscan Orogeny, some crust was depressed deep enough (perhaps about 40 km) to raise the temperature at its base sufficiently to initiate melting.

Sometimes a pulse of heat was delivered from the mantle, and in this connection it is interesting that there is a suite of dykes of unusual composition, known as lampro-phyres, which were intruded just before the granites were formed. Lamprophyres may represent the product of partial melting of the lower crust or mantle, which suggests the development of higher temperatures in the mantle at this time. Elsewhere in the world lamprophyres are often the precursors to the intrusion of granites. Volcanicity in the Exeter area of Early Permian age (about 290 Ma) involved lava flows which also seem to be related to the lamprophyres in composition. A good place to see a lamprophyre dyke is on the north side of Holywell Bay. Lamprophyres are also seen around the Fal estuary, notably near Trelissick. They weather readily to a clay, but often contain large crystals of phlogopite mica.

The Cornubian granites are unusually rich in radioactive uranium and thorium, which could provide another possible source of heat for their initial melting. For this reason they are known as high-heat-producing (HHP) granites. It is possible that the original crust from which the granites were derived could also have been rich in radioactive elements, and hence would have heated up more rapidly.

So, by the final climax of the Variscan Orogeny, some continental crust had been pushed down to a considerable depth and melting commenced. The melting process is called *anatexis*, and what happens is that the lower-melting-point minerals melt first and form a fluid which is squeezed out and begins to accumulate as a separate fluid of granitic composition. This new fluid is of slightly lower density than the surrounding metamorphic rocks. As more granitic fluid accumulates, it begins to form a large balloon of granite magma, surrounded by metamorphic rocks which are sufficiently hot

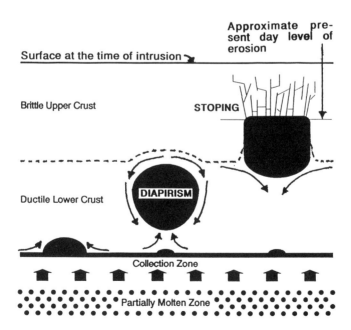

Figure 59 *Diagram to show how molten granite is produced at the base of the crust and then subsequently migrates upwards by diapirism (the surrounding rocks being displaced by flow) and then, at shallower depths, by stoping along lines of weakness such as joints in the brittle upper crust. Diagram kindly supplied by Alan Bromley.*

to be plastic and capable of flow (ductile). The granite mass now begins to float upwards, with the metamorphic rocks yielding by ductile flow around it (*Figure 59*). It is rather like a giant hot-air balloon in very slow motion. This kind of upward movement by flow of the surrounding rocks is known as *diapiric movement*.

When the granite reaches shallower levels in the crust, a different mechanism takes over, because the crust at these higher levels is cooler and no longer capable of ductile flow. In this brittle environment, the mobile molten granite seeks out lines of weakness such as major joints, faults, etc., along which magma is injected. In this way large blocks of **killas** (the term used in Cornwall for rocks of sedimentary origin around the granite) cease to be connected to adjoining blocks and are surrounded by molten granite (*Figure 59*). This process can be clearly seen in places like Rinsey Cove, Wicca Pool, Porthmeor Cove (*Figure 60*) and around Cape Cornwall on the north coast of the Penwith peninsula. As the block of killas has a density slightly higher than that of molten granite, once it is detached from the roof of the granite intrusion it sinks slowly down through the granite to the floor of the intrusion. The granite then proceeds to envelop other higher blocks, and so on, a process known as *stoping*. In this way it is possible for a granite to 'stope' its way to quite shallow levels in the earth's crust, perhaps to within a few kilometres of the surface.

Even at shallow levels the lighter granite was capable of pushing aside the enveloping sedimentary rocks, and the way that the strike of the sedimentary rocks swings around the Land's End, Carnmenellis and Bodmin Moor granites shows clearly how these were deformed by the upward movement of the buoyant granite.

Age of the granites

Granites can be dated by measuring the proportions of various radioactive isotopes present in the constituent minerals, and then comparing them with known half-lives for the isotopes concerned. Methods include determining the ratios of isotopes of potassium/argon, uranium/lead, rubidium/strontium and neodymium/samarium. One of the most recently developed dating methods involves two isotopes of argon (^{39}Ar and ^{40}Ar), and can give results accurate to within a few million years. These dates show that the intrusion of the granites was spread over the surprisingly long period of 30 million years, from approximately 300 Ma to 270 Ma (Late Carboniferous to Early Permian).

Granite mass	Age of intrusion
Isles of Scilly	290-285 Ma
Land's End	280-275 Ma
Carnmenellis	295-290 Ma
St Austell	285-270 Ma
Bodmin Moor	290 Ma
Dartmoor	300-280 Ma

There is, however, no relationship between the position in the orogenic belt and the time of intrusion; the southernmost granite (Land's End, see *Figure 5*) is one of the youngest, and the northernmost (Bodmin Moor) is one of the oldest, which is the opposite of what one might expect from the date of the main deformation in the areas concerned. Of the major granites, Bodmin Moor and Carnmenellis are Late Carbon-

Figure 60 *Porthmeor Cove, on the north side of the Land's End granite, showing the contact between the granite (pale coloured, below) and the dark coloured metamorphic rocks (above). Veins of granite can be seen to extend into the metamorphic rocks along joints and fractures; as these isolate blocks of the slightly denser metamorphic rock (bottom right hand corner), these sink down into the granite – a process known as stoping (see also Figure 59).*

iferous, and St Austell and Land's End are Early Permian (the Carboniferous/Permian boundary is dated at 290 Ma).

The two older granites were intruded during the closing stages of the Variscan Orogeny and hence are locally foliated (foliation = the minerals making up the rock are oriented parallel to one another: look at the kerbstones in River Street, Truro, to see foliated granite). This reflects the stress conditions at or shortly after the time they were intruded. The St Austell and Land's End granite masses appear to be composed of more than one intrusion, separately emplaced at different times.

One fascinating feature of the granites is that the oldest granites (Carnmenellis and Bodmin Moor) appear to be the most deeply eroded, implying that they were originally intruded at a higher level than the younger granites. This may reflect the tendency for the granites to rise to a particular depth below the land surface at the time they were emplaced, so the differences between the earlier and later granites may reflect the fact that the surface below which they were intruded was lowered by erosion during the interval between the two phases of intrusion.

Elvans

Minor intrusions of granitic composition (**elvans**) continued to be intruded as dykes in and around all the main intrusions up to 10 million years after the main granite emplacement event (*Figure 14*). Although the chemical composition of the elvans is similar to the biotite granites, they are much finer in grain, due to rapid cooling and crystallisation. Flow-banding parallel to the margin of an elvan dyke can often be seen.

Many elvans cut across mineral veins, indicating that they are later than the veins; in other places the veins may cut the elvans, so these latter elvans were intruded towards the end of the main phase of metalliferous high-temperature mineralisation. There is a general spatial relationship between the areas where elvans occur and the main areas of mineralisation.

Elvans continue for considerable distances beyond the granites and their meta-morphic aureoles. An elvan at the south end of Watergate Bay is some 10 km from the nearest granite, and an elvan 25 km long reaches the Camel estuary north of Rock, at which point it is 15 km from the nearest part of the Bodmin Moor granite.

As the granite masses are of different ages, so the elvans associated with each also appear to be of different ages. A good example is the Wherry elvan, exposed in a reef to the south of Penzance Harbour and once exploited for its tin content by an offshore mine, often shown in 19th-century pictures of the Penzance shoreline. The nearby Land's End granite is the youngest granite mass in Cornwall and the Wherry elvan has been shown to be older than this, suggesting that it is more likely to be related instead to the older Carnmenellis granite.

In the mineralised belts the elvans generally run parallel to the lodes, but in the area south and west of the St Austell granite, the Start-Perranporth Line seems to have exerted a strong influence on the orientation of the elvans. An almost continuous elvan extends from the northern end of Perran Sands eastwards to near Mitchell, and then continues from near St Stephen to the area near Sticker and Polgooth, where it splits into two to intersect the south coast at Pentewan and the cliffs between Porthpean and Black Head. This may be a case where the magma forming the elvan has used the ancient line of weakness represented by the SPL as a conduit. A north-south elvan extends south from Watergate Bay and is one of the few examples of an elvan following this trend, which is probably the line of one of the cross-course faults referred to earlier.

Volcanic activity associated with the granites

All the granites probably rose to within a few kilometres of the surface. Almost certainly there was some form of surface volcanic activity over each of the main granite masses, but erosion removed all these volcanic edifices long ago. Volcanicity associated with acidic magmas such as granites is usually fairly violent in character, so we must envisage activity like the 1980 eruption of Mount St Helens in the US, or the 1991 eruption of Mount Pinatubo in the Philippines. The Permian breccias of Devon contain abundant fragments of rhyolitic volcanic rocks up to a metre or so in size, and abundant individual feldspar crystals, which must have been derived from the volcanic superstructure which existed above the Dartmoor granite mass at that time. Cornwall also has one small area of this type of breccia at Kingsand, which contains similar fragments of volcanic rock (*Figure 73a*, in Chapter 10).

However, the really important feature at Kingsand is a rhyolite lava flow associated with the breccias; it is well exposed along the foreshore east of the village (*Figure 61*). Not only do we find the flow, but also what appears to be a volcanic 'neck' (*Figure 12d*) at Withnoe, exposed in a small disused quarry above Whitsand Bay. The Withnoe exposure shows vertically flow-banded rhyolite, indicating upward movement in the pipe feeding the vent.

The geochemistry of the Kingsand and Withnoe occurrences suggests that they are most closely related to the elvans associated with the Bodmin Moor granite. This little

Figure 61 *Kingsand rhyolite lava flow of Late Carbon-iferous/Early Permian age, possibly erupted from the Withnoe volcano; note the crude columnar jointing.*

patch of lava and the associated sediments therefore provides us with an insight into what the surface would have been like at the time the granites were being intruded.

Types of granite

There are many different types of granite, both in composition and texture. In particular, the size of the crystals is approximately related to the rate of cooling, although the chemistry of the molten material can also have an influence on crystal size. The coarsest granite is often referred to as a **big-feldspar granite**, and particularly good places to see this type of granite are the quarries in the Luxulyan area.

If you take a piece of this granite and break it so that there is a nice clean face exposed (*Figure 62*), and then examine it with a hand lens, you will see that there are three types of mineral forming the granite – quartz, feldspar and mica. The **quartz**, which is usually grey in colour and has a greasy lustre, is silica, SiO_2. The **feldspar** is usually a creamy off-white colour (in some cases pink) and sometimes shows angular cleavages due to the crystal structure having preferred lines of weakness along which it will break. It has a more complicated composition – $KAlSi_3O_8$ is the composition for orthoclase (*Figure 21c*), which is a potassium feldspar, and $NaAlSi_3O_8$ is the composition for albite, a sodium feldspar. The third mineral is a flaky **mica**, which comes in two common forms: **biotite,** $K(Mg,Fe)_3(AlSi_3O_{10})(OH)_2$, which is an iron-bearing mica, usually black in colour, and **muscovite,** $KAl_2(AlSi_3O_{10})(OH)_2$, which is a

97

Figure 62 *Macro-photograph of Luxulyan granite from Tregarden Quarry. The white mineral is feldspar, the grey is quartz and the dark-coloured shiny mineral is biotite mica. The width of the photograph is about 1 cm.*

transparent flaky potassium-rich mica. In the western part of the St Austell granite and a few other places a lithium-bearing mica, usually coloured various shades of brown, is present. A greenish mica called **gilbertite** is characteristic of many of the altered areas in the granite; it has a composition similar to muscovite, but some of the potassium has been replaced by water molecules.

Other minerals which are commonly found in the granites of South-west England include **tourmaline**, which is a complex mineral containing boron. It is usually black in colour and can be distinguished from biotite by its lack of flaky cleavage and its elongate needle-shaped form, triangular in cross-section. Tourmaline is particularly common in the china-clay pits. Many other minerals are found in the granites: **topaz,** a fluorine-bearing mineral, not of gem quality unfortunately; **fluorite,** calcium fluoride; **apatite,** a phosphate mineral; and ore minerals such as the tin-containing **cassiterite** and the tungsten-containing **wolframite**.

Granites crystallise in different ways, according to the pressure and temperature conditions at the time of their formation. The amount of water present and small amounts of elements such as fluorine, boron and lithium will also affect the way it crystallises. If a molten granite magma is cooled very rapidly it will not crystallise at all, but will form a glass – **obsidian**. The Kingsand lava flow was probably, at least in part, originally a glass. Given time, a glass will gradually crystallise, but the cryst-allites so formed are usually of microscopic size. This process is known as devitri-fication and can sometimes be seen in ancient man-made glass. The felsitic elvan dykes are of granitic composition and were intruded after the main period of granite intrusion; these sometimes show spherulitic devitrification at their margins, so they must also have cooled rapidly as a glass, indicating that the granite itself was relatively cool by the time they were intruded.

There are fine-grained and coarse-grained granites, and often the fine-grained types appear to be the later phase. A granite which contains particularly large crystals is called *megacrystic* and the so-called big-feldspar granite contains orthoclase feldspar crystals up to 15 cm long. This is often found near the roof and around the margins of the intrusions, indicating that the conditions in these areas were especially suitable for the growth of large feldspar crystals.

Occasionally late-stage magmatic fluids will appear with a composition which enables very large crystals of all the constituent minerals to develop – these are known as **pegmatites**. They form dyke-like and sill-like masses within the granite and the adjoining country rocks. Sometimes the kind of fluids which form pegmatites crystallise with a finer-grained texture; they are then known as **aplites**.

Details of individual granites

We will describe these working from the east towards the west (*Figure 5*):

The **Kit Hill** and **Hingston Down granites** are two small cusps of biotite granite which appear to lie on a buried granite ridge connecting the Bodmin Moor and Dartmoor granites. Isotopic dating suggests these intrusions were early, intruded between 280 and 290 Ma. The active Hingston Down quarry provides a fine exposure of one of these granites.

The **Bodmin Moor granite** is one of the earliest of the granites (287-288 Ma) and is entirely composed of biotite granite, mostly of the standard megacrystic type, with irregular patches of fine-grained granite in the centre around Dozmary Pool and north of Bolventor. On the west side, in De Lank and Hantergantick quarries, the granite can be seen to be foliated like a gneiss which suggests that this early granite was influenced by stresses associated with the closing stages of the Variscan Orogeny, as it was crystallising.

Normal faults aligned WSW-ENE tangentially cut the northern and southern parts of the granite, suggesting that the central part of the granite has been raised relative to the northern and southern shoulders. This may be due to a tendency for the lighter granite to rise relative to the slightly denser country rocks around it. The orientation of these normal faults suggests that they were formed in a similar north-south extensional regime to that which pertained when the main metalliferous mineralisation was taking place, and the two may be of similar age. A quartz vein standing up as a tor-like mass is seen along the line of the northern fault at Lanlavery Rock, just over a mile northeast of Rough Tor, and at the dramatic crags of Devils Jump, 2 miles south of Camelford..

Tors are found mainly on the eastern and northern side of the granite; Brown Willy, one of the tors, is the highest point in Cornwall and the tor forming the Cheesewring is particularly picturesque (*Figure 13*). The origin of tors is discussed in Chapter 12.

Elvan dykes are fairly common in the mineralised tract in the southern part of the granite, especially in the mineralised area around the Caradon and Phoenix mines where they fill fault fissures in the granite. Elvan dykes are particularly good at showing the displacement caused by cross-courses, as in Park St Neot china-clay pit, and at Temple, on Bodmin Moor, where offshoots from the Portwrinkle Fault show a small dextral displacement. One particularly long elvan extends for about 25 km from Davidstow Woods to Rock on the Camel estuary.

The St Austell granite is the most complex of the Cornish granites and by far the most important economically (*Figure 63*). It has been one of the main engines driving the Cornish economy for over 2000 years! The granite can be divided into two parts:

The **eastern part**, around Helman Tor and Luxulyan, is a fairly standard biotite granite whose age is around 282 Ma. Some of the granite is coarsely megacrystic, with large orthoclase feldspar crystals up to 15 cm in length, as can be seen around Luxulyan and on Helman Tor. This makes it a highly attractive dimension (building) stone and it was extensively worked in and around the Luxulyan valley in the 19th century.

One of the geological curiosities associated with the Luxulyan area is **luxullianite**, which is a handsome rock consisting of pink orthoclase set in a matrix of radiating black tourmaline crystals (*Figure 24d*, page 34). The Duke of Wellington's sarcophagus in St Paul's Cathedral is made of luxullianite, and it still occurs in Tregarden Quarry; aggregate produced from this quarry will often be found to contain fragments of luxullianite.

Deep weathering in the geological past has produced large rounded boulders of granite in the Luxulyan area, which are seen in many of the fields around the village, where they look like huge sleeping animals.

The **western part** of the St Austell granite is the younger, and ranges in age from 275 Ma to 270 Ma. It is composed of a great variety of granite types, some of which are quite unusual. Two isolated cusps of granite, at Belowda Beacon and Castle-an-Dinas, on the north side of Goss Moor, also appear to be related to it.

This western part of the St Austell granite is by far the most important source of china clay in Europe. Part of the reason for this lies in the nature of the granite, for a lithium mica takes the place of biotite over much of the outcrop, and there is a higher proportion of sodium feldspar than elsewhere; this will be discussed further in Chapter 9. Besides the lithium-mica granite, there is also a topaz granite which, as the name implies, is rich in the fluorine-bearing mineral topaz. Yet another variety is the fluorite granite, although there is still debate over whether the fluorite is a genuine primary mineral, or if it has been formed by an alteration process operating after the granite had crystallised. Topaz and fluorite granites form two masses in the Nanpean-Treviscoe and Hensbarrow areas (see *Figure 63*), where they appear to be slightly younger than the lithium-mica granites. China stone, which has a very low content of iron-bearing dark minerals, is obtained from these granites (see Chapter 3).

There are a number of exotic pegmatites in the St Austell granite, including the 'stockscheider' pegmatite (*Figure 71*) in Goonbarrow china-clay pit with its feathery curved orthoclase-feldspar growths; the Trelavour Downs pegmatite with pink feldspar and large sheaves of lithium-rich biotite up to 15 cm long, often seen in mineral collections from the St Austell area; and the Tresayes pegmatite, which contains feldspar crystals the size of a football, which was formerly worked as an ingredient for glass manufacture – hence the local name 'The Glass Mine'.

The youngest 'proper' granites are found at Castle-an-Dinas (268 Ma), where a younger granite cuts out an older north-south wolfram lode, and in the western lobe of the granite south of Indian Queens, where a granite magma was contemporaneous with the Wheal Remfry breccia, dated at 270 Ma. This appears to be the youngest granite in the whole batholith, but it rests on only two age determinations and we still do not

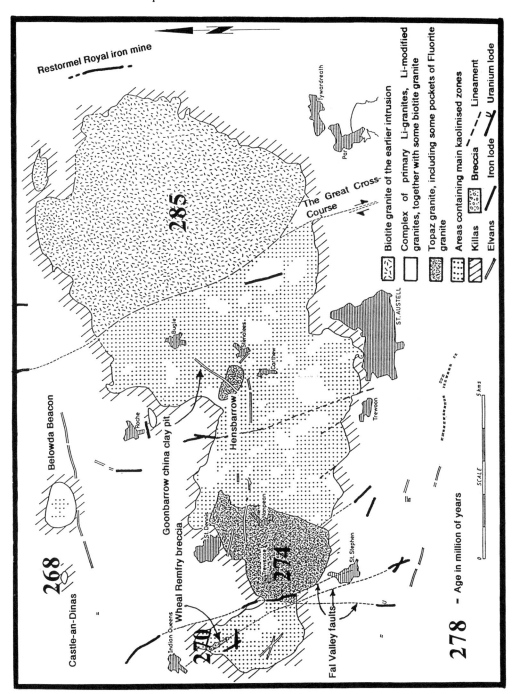

Figure 63 Geological map of the St Austell granite, showing many of the features and locations mentioned in the text. Partly based on the 1:50,000 Sheet 347, published by the British Geological Survey (reproduced by permission of the Director, British Geological Survey, NERC copyright reserved).

know how extensive the 268-270 Ma intrusive phase was. We will return to the formation of the Wheal Remfry breccia later (page 108).

The Wheal Remfry breccia and the associated granite are cut by an elvan dyke (*Figure 14*), so granite magmatism continued for some time after 270 Ma. Elvans, usually in the form of dykes, are widespread in and around the St Austell granite and are seen in nearly every china-clay pit. At Pentewan an elvan was worked from early times as a source of durable, easily carved freestone. This elvan can be seen from the coastal footpath in the cliffs between Pentewan and Hallane.

The **Carnmenellis granite** is of similar age (290 Ma) to the Bodmin Moor granite. Two smaller granite areas adjoin the main outcrop: the **Carn Brea** mass, immediately to the south of Camborne, is of a similar age to the main granite, and deep-lode mining has shown that the two merge at depth. However, the circular **Carn Marth** intrusion, north of the main granite, appears to be several million years younger and may therefore represent a separate intrusive phase. Intriguingly, samples from the bottom of the geothermal boreholes 2 km deep at Rosemanowes, in the southeastern part of the granite, give younger ages still, suggesting that it took several million years longer for the deeper parts of the intrusion to cool sufficiently to begin to crystallise.

Most of the Carnmenellis granite is a megacrystic biotite granite, although there are several areas of fine-grained granite within it. The different types of granite form concentric rings, one inside the other, which can be seen on the new 1:50,000-scale geological map for Sheet 352 (Falmouth) published by the British Geological Survey. The Carnmenellis granite sometimes shows a preferred orientation of the constituent minerals (foliation), giving it a gneiss-like appearance; this was well seen in the road cuttings made for the new Penryn by-pass, and indicates that the granite crystallised under stress.

Minor intrusions occur north of the Carnmenellis granite and appear to lie on a buried spur of granite extending northwards at shallow depth under the killas. The presence of this ridge of granite is given away by a band of thermally metamorphosed rocks, the metamorphic aureole, linking the Carnmenellis granite through Porthtowan and on to St Agnes and Cligga Head, near Perranporth.

The most intense zone of tin and copper mineralisation in the whole of the Cornubian orefield lies on the northern flanks of the Carnmenellis granite. Cornwall's one remaining tin mine – South Crofty – lies in this area.

The **St Agnes granite** is small (500 x 250 m) and lies just west of St Agnes Beacon. The small disused Cameron Quarry at the northern end of the granite outcrop shows intensely greisened and mineralised granite, with some evidence of metalliferous mineralisation. The **Cligga Head granite** is of similar size, but the western half of the intrusion has been eroded away and lies under the sea. The cross-section through the remaining half is spectacularly exposed in the cliffs to the south of Cligga Head. Not far from the top of the cliffs is the well-known exposure of greisen-bordered veins (*Figure 64*). Sheeted joints show a 'synform' and 'antiform' structure, which can be clearly seen in the cliffs. Elvan dykes are also present. A tungsten mine operated on these cliffs during the Second World War, when this strategic metal was needed for armaments. Both of these small intrusions contain granite of the highly evolved type, as at St Austell and Godolphin. Still further north, in the cliffs immediately west of Perranporth, the top of yet another minor cusp of granite is seen in a sea cave.

Figure 64 *Cligga Head: a greisen-bordered sheeted-vein system, each vein represent-ing a crack produced by chemically-laden pressurised fluids, which then moved along the crack altering the walls by processes known as greisening and tourmalinisation (see Chapter 9).*

The Tregonning-Godolphin granite, 3 miles west of Helston, is one of the smaller granite masses and, like the St Austell mass, contains lithium-mica variants as well as more normal biotite granites. It is younger than the Carnmenellis granite, at 280 Ma, and has been suggested to represent an evolved magma ultimately derived from that granite. Exposures in the cliffs near Megiliggar Rocks show spectacular pegmatite-aplite-granite sheets cutting metamorphosed Mylor Slates in the roof zone of the intrusion. Some of the mineralisation in the vicinity of this granite has recently been shown to be older than the granite, suggesting that it was associated with the Carnmenellis granite before the Tregonning-Godolphin granite was intruded. Tregonning Hill is where William Cookworthy made his original discovery of china clay in 1746, but there has been no working here since before the Second World War.

Between the Tregonning-Godolphin granite and the Land's End granite lies the tiny cusp of granite which forms the southern part of **St Michael's Mount,** extending southwards under the sea. This is yet another of the evolved granites, like St Agnes and Cligga Head, and shows a beautifully developed stockwork of east-west greisen-bordered veins with cassiterite, wolframite, stannite and copper mineralisation on the wave cut platform on the south side of the Mount, together with other rare and unusual minerals. Not surprisingly, the National Trust bans hammers from this locality!

The **Land's End granite** appears to be the youngest of the major granites in South-west England, with the exception of the Lundy granite, which is much younger (Tertiary). It is entirely a biotite granite, with several large areas of a fine-grained variety in the central area. It has recently been suggested that it is composed of two separate intrusions, rather like the St Austell granite. The earliest phase (278 Ma) is

Figure 65 *Granite tor on St Mary's, Isles of Scilly.*

thought to be the Zennor lobe, forming the northeastern part of the granite mass, and the younger phase (275 Ma) is the St Buryan lobe which forms the southern intrusion and is partly covered, on its western side, by the waters of the Atlantic Ocean.

The metamorphic aureole is superbly displayed on the northern side of the Penwith peninsula. The mineral lodes of the St Just area are in an anomalous direction – NW-SE – reflecting the fact that they must have been some of the last main-stage tin/copper mineral veins to be formed, possibly at a time when the stress conditions had changed to those represented by the cross-course veins in other granite masses.

The **Isles of Scilly granite** (*Figure 65*) is another biotite granite and we do not see the contact with the metamorphosed Palaeozoic rocks anywhere on the present islands. Offshore survey work suggests this is an oblong granite about the same size as Bodmin Moor and Carnmenellis. There is little dating information on it: what there is suggests that it belongs to the older group including Carnmenellis and Bodmin Moor. There is also not a great deal of variation in the nature of the granite, apart from a fine-grained area in the centre of the intrusion (Samson and southernmost Tresco), and aplites and a large elvan near Hugh Town, on St Mary's. The Isles of Scilly granite is unique in that no significant metalliferous mineralisation is known to be associated with it.

Marine seismic and gravity geophysical studies in the area of continental shelf west of the Scillies suggest that the batholith continues as a buried ridge for some distance west of the islands. Under the waters of the Celtic Sea, to the north of the line of the Cornubian batholith, there is another smaller batholith of similar age, centred around the undersea shoal known as **Haig Fras**: two granite masses are known to be exposed on the sea floor. Underwater exploration has revealed ghostly tor-like features, suggesting that once this was dry land, subject to the kind of weathering that affected the granites of the Cornubian batholith.

9

The Cornubian orefield: alteration and mineralisation of the granites after intrusion

Even as the granites were still crystallising, the processes which were to lead to the formation of one of the world's greatest concentrations of mineral wealth were already at work.

Following emplacement, each granite mass underwent similar processes of alteration and mineralisation. But these processes were probably taking place in and around the early granites *before* the later ones had been intruded so, in places, a later phase of mineralisation related to one of the younger granites can be found superimposed on an older set of mineral veins related to an earlier granite.

Some of the mineral deposits were already in the rocks before the granites were intruded, such as the manganese ore deposits formerly exploited in the Launceston area. These deposits were formed by processes (both sedimentary and volcanic) on the sea bottom and/or metamorphic processes during the Variscan Orogeny.

Metalliferous mineralisation

Let us look at how a typical granite would have evolved and become mineralised and altered. The St Austell granite is a particularly good example, as it is well exposed in the china-clay pits and involves all the stages we are going to discuss. *Figure 66* is a series of cartoon cross-sections to show how the granites evolved after their emplacement, and how they became subsequently mineralised and altered. The granites of the Cornubian batholith are high-heat-producing (HHP) because they are relatively rich in heat-producing radioactive elements such as uranium and thorium. This heat was sufficient to prolong the cooling of the granite considerably.

The following table gives some idea of the kinds of metalliferous mineral deposits which formed as the granite cooled:

Pegmatitic and aplitic mineral deposits (Sn/W)	500-600°C
Greisen-bordered sheeted-vein systems (Sn/W)	400-450°C
Main-stage Sn/Cu mineralisation	350-450°C
Cross-course Fe/Pb/Ag/Zn mineralisation	200-350°C

(Sn = tin, W = tungsten, Cu = copper, Fe = iron, Pb = lead, Ag = silver, Zn = zinc)

Pegmatitic and aplitic mineral deposits. As the crystals of feldspar, quartz and mica formed in the granite magma, so a residual fluid began to develop, which was different in composition to the original granite melt. Sometimes this crystallised to form sheets of coarsely crystalline pegmatite and finer-grained aplite, which may contain metalliferous tin- and tungsten-bearing minerals such as cassiterite and wolframite. Pegmatites can be seen in china-clay pits such as Goonbarrow and Gunheath, and in many coastal exposures of granite, such as Rinsey Cove and Megiligar Rocks in

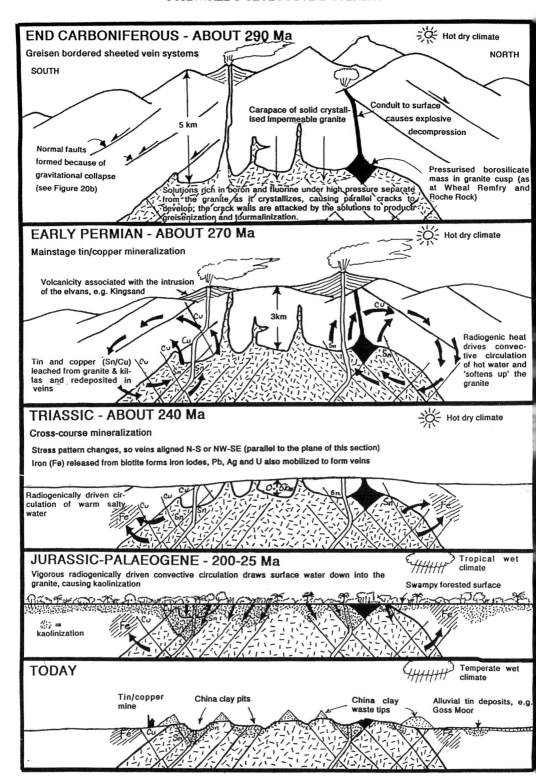

END CARBONIFEROUS - ABOUT 290 Ma

☀ Hot dry climate

Greisen bordered sheeted vein systems

SOUTH

NORTH

5 km

Carapace of solid crystallised impermeable granite

Conduit to surface
causes explosive
decompression

Normal faults
formed because of
gravitational collapse
(see Figure 20b)

Pressurised borosilicate
mass in granite cusp (as
at Wheal Remfry and
Roche Rock)

Solutions rich in boron and fluorine under high pressure separate
from the granite as it crystallizes, causing parallel cracks to
develop; the crack walls are attacked by the solutions to produce
greisenization and tourmalinization.

EARLY PERMIAN - ABOUT 270 Ma

☀ Hot dry climate

Mainstage tin/copper mineralization

Volcanicity associated with the intrusion
of the elvans, e.g. Kingsand

3km

Tin and copper (Sn/Cu)
leached from granite & killas and redeposited in
veins

Radiogenic heat
drives convec-
tive circulation
of hot water and
'softens up' the
granite

TRIASSIC - ABOUT 240 Ma

☀ Hot dry climate

Cross-course mineralization

Stress pattern changes, so veins aligned N-S or NW-SE (parallel to the plane of this section)

Iron (Fe) released from biotite forms iron lodes, Pb, Ag and U also mobilized to form veins

Radiogenically driven circulation of warm salty
water

JURASSIC-PALAEOGENE - 200-25 Ma

☂ Tropical wet
climate

Vigorous radiogenically driven convective circulation draws surface water down into the
granite, causing kaolinization

Swampy forested surface

⠿ =
kaolinization

TODAY

☂ Temperate wet
climate

Tin/copper
mine

China clay pits

China clay
waste tips

Alluvial tin deposits, e.g.
Goss Moor

the Tregonning-Godolphin granite, and the various coves around Cape Cornwall. In South Crofty tin mine they sometimes contain useful ore values.

Greisen-bordered sheeted-vein systems. The granite crystallised from the top down, so a layer of already-crystallised granite (*Figure 66*, top) formed at the margin of the upper part of the intrusion, thereby sealing in the still crystallising magma in the interior of the granite mass. As solid crystals formed, the vapour pressure in the remaining fluid increased dramatically. This produced a kind of 'pressure cooker' effect, with a high internal pressure developing within the granite mass. At the same time cooling led to an overall contraction.

These two effects caused the semi-solid crystal mush in the interior of the intrusion to develop cracks, along which the late-stage fluids began to circulate. The regional stresses affecting the granite governed the direction in which the cracks developed and propagated, so that cracking took place perpendicular to the direction of least stress. Most of the orefield seems to have developed during the period of north-south extension which accompanied the gravitational collapse of the Variscan mountains, so the direction of least stress was generally N-S or NW-SE, resulting in cracks developing in an E-W or SW-NE direction.

The chemically aggressive residual hot fluids left over after the crystallisation of most of the granite now began to circulate vigorously along the cracks in the granite, causing the rock alongside the cracks to be altered. The *hydrothermal* (= hot water) fluids were solutions rich in boron, fluorine and silica. One alteration process involved the replacement of the feldspar in the granite by quartz and mica, sometimes with the fluorine-bearing mineral topaz as well, a process known as **greisening**. Another process involved the wholesale replacement of the original granite minerals by tourmaline (an aluminium-silicate mineral containing boron) and is called **tourmalinisation,** akin to the formation of luxullianite, mentioned in Chapter 8 (page 101).

The stresses that led to the formation of the cracks often led to many parallel cracks forming, so we find swarms of veins (**sheeted-vein systems**) developing, as is beautifully displayed at Cligga Head (*Figure 64*), on the south side of St Michael's Mount, and in china-clay pits such as Goonbarrow. The original crack along which the altering fluids flowed is usually marked by a narrow **leader** composed of coarsely crystalline quartz and tourmaline, with the more conspicuous greisened and tourmalinised zones on either side of the leader. Metalliferous mineralisation can occur in the leader and may also be dispersed through the greisen borders to the veins as well, although it is often hard to detect with the naked eye. Many veins are composite, having been repeatedly reopened by fresh pulses of mineralising fluids.

Although tourmalinisation and greisening usually border veins, sometimes a whole area of granite seems to have become 'waterlogged' with the altering fluids, so that large irregularly shaped masses of greisened and tourmalinised granite developed, as can be seen in many china-clay pits and at locations such as Cameron Quarry in the St Agnes granite. Masses of greisen composed largely of quartz and topaz ('topazfels') often occur at the contact between the granite and the surrounding killas (meta-

Figure 66 (opposite)   A series of cartoon cross-sections to show how the Cornish granites evolved after their emplacement, and how they were subsequently mineralised and altered. Based primarily on the St Austell granite, although much the same sequence applies for the other granites.

Figure 67 *Roche Rock: a mass of schorl composed of tourmaline and quartz, formed by a boron-rich fluid accumulating in a granite cusp. A 15th-century chapel, dedicated to St Michael, surmounts the rock.*

sedimentary rocks) as can be seen at St Mewan Beacon near Trewoon (St Austell) and at Carliquoiter Rocks near Retew, at the westernmost end of the St Austell granite.

There is much discussion currently over whether a separate 'immiscible' borosilicate fluid developed in the granite (oil and water are immiscible, i.e. they will not mix). In many of the china-clay pits, 'blobs' of tourmaline and quartz ranging in size from a gooseberry up to several metres across appear to be 'floating' in the granite, sometimes concentrated at the contact between two different phases of the intrusion (*Figure 71*), as can be seen in Goonbarrow clay pit. It is also evident that large masses of borosilicate fluid accumulated in the cusps on the upper surface of the granite, and when this crystallised it yielded a rock composed of quartz and tourmaline, known as **schorl**. Roche Rock (*Figure 67*) is composed of schorl in an outlying cusp of the granite.

At Wheal Remfry something much more dramatic seems to have happened to one of these large borosilicate masses. Here, a large mass about 500 m long and up to 100 m wide had accumulated along a line of weakness caused by one of the faults belonging to the Fal Valley Fault Zone. It appears that it was under considerable pressure and that the fluid somehow managed to establish a conduit to the land surface, perhaps triggered by an earthquake, causing the borosilicate material accompanied by some granite magma to rush up to the surface, rather like champagne rushing out of the bottle as the cork pops. Once the pressure had been dissipated a lot of the material which had rushed up the pipe fell back down again and set solid as a mass of granite and killas fragments in a fine-grained matrix of tourmaline and quartz. This very dramatic-looking rock (*Figure 68*) is known as the Wheal Remfry breccia, dated at 270 Ma. There is evidence to suggest that it became pressurised and depressurised several times in succession; its effect at the surface must have been some form of blast of boron-rich material from a vent. Perhaps some Early Permian creatures trotting around in the Variscan mountains minding their own business got a big surprise!

Figure 68   *The Wheal Remfry breccia (on the right): granite and killas fragments set in a matrix of tourmaline and quartz, probably formed by explosive depressurisation of a borosilicate mass which had accumulated along one of the Fal Valley faults.*

Some mineralisation outside the granite probably accompanied the formation of the sheeted-vein systems. **Stockworks** are composed of many fine veins criss-crossing one another, and examples such as the Mulberry stockwork near Lanivet, Parka and the Fatwork-and-Virtue stockworks just south of Indian Queens, and Grylls Bunny above Botallack, may be associated with the early development of the sheeted-vein systems.

Main-stage Sn/Cu mineralisation. This stage is really an extension of the activity we have already described above for the sheeted-vein systems (*Figure 66* – Early Permian). The main difference is that substantial quantities of water from outside the granite were now incorporated in the fluids circulating in and around the granite, and the heat from radioactive elements started to have a significant effect on the pattern of circulation. Computer-based simulations of how fluids would circulate in the granites, assuming they were covered by 3 km of sedimentary rocks, show that convection cells would have developed; and strong upward flow appears to correspond with areas of intense mineralisation – the so-called 'emanative centres'.

Some crystals contain tiny bubbles of fluid trapped within them from the time of their formation: these **fluid inclusions** give evidence of conditions at that time. Study of these shows that the fluids responsible for the mineralisation were saline; partly because the original magmatic fluids had been saline, and partly because the surface at this time would have been arid and hot, resulting in natural groundwater which was saline. This water was capable of dissolving out metals from one place and depositing them elsewhere, either where it was cooler, or where two waters of different chemistry met, causing the metalliferous minerals to be precipitated. Tin may have come partly from the granite itself and partly from the Devonian sedimentary rocks; much of the copper is likely to have been leached out of basic Devonian igneous rocks.

The circulating water mainly moved along fractures associated with the continuing collapse of the Variscan mountain chain, and the minerals were deposited in these fractures. The main tin-bearing mineral was **cassiterite** (*Figure 20b*) and this was deposited in the higher temperature areas; copper minerals were deposited at slightly lower temperatures, usually in the form of **chalcopyrite** (*Figure 20a*). If a single rich copper vein is followed down it will sometimes give way at depth to tin mineralisation, as was found in many of the mines in the Camborne-Redruth area and in mines of the Par-St Blazey-Holmbush area. However, there is evidence that these veins were repeatedly pressurised and depressurised by the fluids and that, if a conduit remained open for a long time, the character of the ores formed would change. So there is much telescoping of the metal zones and often successive phases are superimposed on one another, giving a very confused picture. Some greisening accompanied these veins, and metal values are often found in the country rocks on either side of the vein. Later weathering has affected most copper lodes (*Figure 69*).

The main-stage mineralisation of the St Just-in-Penwith mineral field is aligned in a cross-course direction, i.e. NW-SE, suggesting that this, the latest main-stage mineralisation in the Cornubian orefield, was formed after the stress direction had changed (see Cross-course Mineralisation, below).

We should not forget that some of the main-stage lodes are cut by elvan dykes, so the final magmatic events can post-date some of the main-stage mineralisation. There is a school of thought which believes that the pulse of heat which produced the elvans was an important contributory factor in this mineralisation.

Small quantities of other minerals were also laid down in the vein systems, for example arsenic and zinc. Along with the valuable, mainly metalliferous minerals, other '*gangue*' minerals were laid down, such as quartz and chlorite. Sometimes these gangue minerals are valuable as a by-product, for example fluorspar and barytes.

This book is not the place for a lengthy description of the mineralogy of Cornish lodes, and the reader is referred to the numerous other publications which cover this aspect of the geology (see page 142 for a reading list). Moreover, most of the metal-bearing main-stage mineralisation lodes have been quarried away in the coastal exposures, and most of the old dumps have been so thoroughly scoured by mineral collectors that it is difficult nowadays to find good specimens except in active mines, quarries and china-clay pits.

Cross-course Fe/Pb mineralisation has attracted much attention in recent years and dating has suggested that this phase took place some time after the intrusion of the granites, mainly during Triassic times at around 240 Ma. By the beginning of the Triassic Period the Variscan mountains would have been considerably lowered by a combination of gravitational collapse and erosion, so the cover of sedimentary rocks on top of the granites would probably have been reduced to around half a kilometre (*Figure 66* – Triassic).

The original magmatic heat of the granite would have been entirely dissipated by this time and the only heat arising from within the granite would have come from the decay of radioactive elements. Climatic conditions during the Triassic were hot and

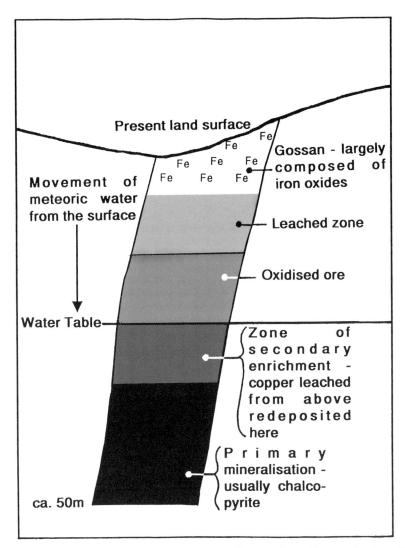

Figure 69 *Diagram to illustrate how a copper vein was altered by weathering. Some of this weathering may have been associated with the tropical climates of the Mesozoic and Palaeogene. Diagram kindly provided by Simon Camm.*

arid, just as in the previous Permian Period. The tectonic stress regime, the complex of forces acting in that part of the crust, changed so that the least horizontal stress was now E-W or SW-NE. This meant that any veins or fractures which formed were in a N-S or NW-SE direction. These are known as the 'cross-course' lodes as they 'cross' the main-stage lodes approximately at right angles. Frequently a small amount of strike-slip fault movement is associated with the cross-courses, usually dextral, but whether this is contemporary with the formation of the lodes, or much later in the Mesozoic or Tertiary, is difficult to tell. Many of the cross-course veins follow earlier faults which were established in the Variscan Orogeny.

The fluids circulating at this stage were of lower temperature and so no tin or tungsten mineralisation is found; there was no boron in the fluids, so tourmaline is absent as well. Generally these lodes are characterised by the presence of large amounts of iron oxides such as **haematite** (a mineral name derived from the blood-red colour of many specimens), some of which may have been derived from the surface, which would have been a 'red' desert, but much was probably derived from iron-bearing micas such as biotite. Huge quantities of iron were removed from the micas of the St Austell granite and moved out along the lines of the cross-courses, which seem to have acted like rubble-filled drains. When the fluids reached the cooler killas surrounding the granite, the iron was precipitated and iron lodes were laid down, forming a ring of such lodes around the St Austell granite (*Figure 63*). Some of the iron mines, such as the Restormel Royal Iron Mine north of Lostwithiel (*Figure 21a*), were commercially quite important, and this was one of very few mines which Queen Victoria and Prince Albert visited underground. The name 'Royal' was bestowed in recognition of their visit.

Other minerals found in these lodes include lead and zinc such as was exploited at East Wheal Rose, 4 miles from Perranporth. Sometimes the lead was highly argentiferous (*Figure 21e*) and much silver could be recovered from it, as in the medieval workings of the lead/silver lodes of the Bere Alston area.

Iron and uranium often are fellow-travellers, so we find that most uranium deposits are in cross-course lodes. The most famous uranium mine in Britain was at South Terras, near St Stephen, on one of the Fal Valley faults (*Figure 63*). Uranium leached from the granite was carried by the flow of water out of the granite along the fault, eventually rising towards the surface and cooling; this caused the uranium to be deposited as a lode of pitchblende, together with other brightly coloured secondary uranium minerals such as autunite (yellow) and torbernite (apple green, *Figure 21g*). The uranium was extracted before the value of the metal to the nuclear industry was known, and it was mainly used to colour glass green.

Kaolinisation – the formation of china clay

The question of how the economically important china clay deposits of Cornwall and Devon (*Figure 72*) came to be formed has exercised the minds of geologists for many years. In the 19th and early 20th centuries there were two opposing views:

- Those who thought that kaolinisation was caused by rising hot, chemical-laden gases and hydrothermal fluids.

- Those who believed the clay had been formed as a result of deep weathering during a past geological time when the climate was hot and humid.

It is now clear that a whole sequence of events was needed, the earliest of which would have been under hydrothermal conditions and the latest of which was probably a form of deep weathering.

The character of the granite is important in controlling the quality of the china clay formed. Much of the younger granite in the western part of the St Austell granite is unusual (*Figure 63*), because a lithium mica takes the place of the more normal biotite mica. This is important, because biotite tends to release iron oxide during kaolinisation, colouring the resulting china clay yellow, brown or red, which is commercially undesirable as whiteness is one of china clay's most important properties.

As we have seen, the granites all underwent extensive alteration by various fluids circulating in the granite (*Figure 66*). Initially, the source of heat was from the cooling granite itself, and saline fluids and gases rich in boron, fluorine and silica formed the quartz-tourmaline veins which are often seen in china-clay pits. Although very little clay appears to have formed at this early stage, nevertheless the granite was probably 'softened-up' for the later kaolinisation (*Figure 66* – Permian).

During the period when the cross-course lodes were being formed the fluids were highly saline (*Figure 66* – Triassic), possibly reflecting the fact that rock salt was being formed at many locations elsewhere in the British Isles at this time. The distribution of the kaolinised zones suggests that some clay may have been formed alongside these 'cross-course' veins although, under high-salinity conditions, it is unlikely to have been kaolinite, but some other clay mineral such as illite (clay mica) and/or smectite (an expanding-lattice clay mineral).

In the Late Triassic, the climate became wetter and fresh water from the surface entered the system resulting in slow convective circulation of fresh water through the granite driven by radiogenic heat (*Figure 66* – Jurassic-Palaeogene). Periodic earth movements opened fractures, which further enabled the water to circulate freely through the granite.

This constant circulation of water over hundreds of millions of years altered the granite, particularly where the earlier alteration phases had softened it up by incipient alteration. Hard granite, originally composed of quartz, feldspar and mica, was altered to a soft china-clay rock. Most of the kaolinite is derived from the alteration of feldspars, the sodium-feldspar being more readily altered than the potassium-feldspar (*Figure 21c*). Earlier-formed smectite was also altered to kaolinite and, under intense kaolinisation, mica was altered as well.

The formation of china clay continued right through the time of the dinosaurs (Jurassic and Cretaceous), when the South-west peninsula formed 'the Cornubian Island' set in a tropical sea (see next chapter), and probably continues slowly even at the present day. China clay appears to have formed on the downward limbs of the con-vection cells, and the drawing down of surface-derived fluids rich in organic substances may have been an important factor in accelerating the kaolinisation.

Deep kaolinisation caused by weathering, formed at the same time as the china clay deposits of South-west England, is known from many parts of the world. It is likely that much china clay would have formed under conditions which are on the borderline between 'weathering' and 'hydrothermal', so it is a rather futile semantic argument to try and decide which is the more important process. Two generations of kaolinite are usually present (*Figure 70*):

- A 'groundmass' kaolinite, which is very fine grained and has been the traditional source of china clay.

- Large curled stacks of kaolinite up to one-tenth of a millimetre in diameter. These appear to have grown in place from solutions moving through the altered granite and can now be recovered by froth-flotation from the refining residues, and ground to make additional product.

During kaolinisation, approximately 25% by weight of the granite is lost, mainly in the form of alkalis (potassium, sodium, magnesium and calcium) and silica. The formation of clay minerals is essentially a process of hydrolysis, with the clay minerals

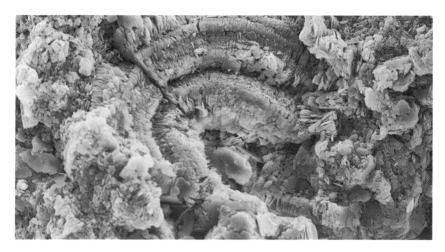

Figure 70   *Scanning electron microscope photograph of china clay as it occurs in the ground before processing. Kaolinite is the main mineral forming china clay, occurring as pseudo-hexagonal plates which can be seen around the periphery; in the centre is a large curled stack of kaolinite, and layers forming individual plates can be clearly seen. The picture is about 0.15 mm wide.*

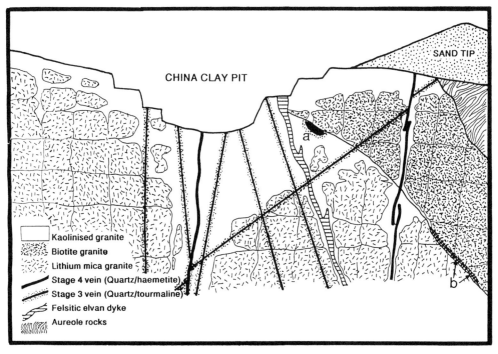

Figure 71   *Generalised cross-section to show the typical features of the geology in a china-clay pit. Any tin or tungsten mineralisation would occur in the Stage 3 quartz-tourmaline veins; the greisening and tourmalinisation associated with these veins is indicated by stippling.* **a** *– borosilicate segregation,* **b** *– 'stockscheider' pegmatite*

114

Figure 72 *A monitor at work in the Goonbarrow china-clay pit. The soft, white kaolinised granite is worked by high-pressure water jets known as monitors. Some steeply inclined dark quartz-tourmaline veins can be seen at the rear.*

containing more water than the rock-forming minerals such as feldspar which preceded them, i.e.:

$$2NaAlSi_3O_8 + 3H_2O = Al_2Si_2O_5(OH)_4 + 4SiO_2 + 2Na(OH)$$

Feldspar   water   kaolinite   silica   alkaline hydroxide

As kaolinisation involved water moving down into the granite, the china-clay deposits generally take the form of funnels, widening upwards towards the surface (*Figure 71*). Occasionally, unkaolinised granite is found overlying kaolinised granite, which is usually due to the footwall granite being chemically more susceptible to kaolinisation than the hanging-wall granite. The stems of the funnels descend to considerable depths, as much as 250 m in a few cases, but more typically 100 m. The deeper underground metalliferous mines rarely encountered any significant kaolinisation, emphasising that this is essentially a surface-oriented process.

The most important areas of kaolinisation are in the western half of the St Austell granite (*Figure 63*), but commercially exploitable deposits also occur in the south-western part of the Dartmoor granite at Lee Moor, and also on Bodmin Moor. Smaller occurrences have been exploited in the past in most of the other granite masses of South-west England.

Changing demand for minerals will no doubt influence the way mining activity develops in the future. Perhaps in years to come reprocessing of the vast china-clay waste tips will yield raw materials which we presently regard as of little value.

10 The Cornubian Island during the time of the dinosaurs

The long time interval between the formation of the Variscan mountains (290 Ma) and the extinction of the dinosaurs (65 Ma) includes the last period of the Palaeozoic Era – the Permian, plus the whole of the Mesozoic Era (Mesozoic = middle age of life). This is a great blank in Cornwall's geological history, because there are no rocks onshore in present-day Cornwall that represent the 180 million year time-span of the Mesozoic. However, there are many clues which can help us to reconstruct what Cornwall may have looked like, and events in the Mesozoic had an important influence on the way today's scenery developed.

The **Permian** was the last period of the Palaeozoic Era (see *Figure 1*), and it was terminated by a major extinction event during which many classes of creatures disappeared. The **Mesozoic** consists of three periods; the oldest is the **Triassic** (245-208 Ma), a period of searing hot deserts; then there was the **Jurassic** (208-145 Ma) with a warm moist climate; and finally the youngest period was the **Cretaceous** (145-65 Ma), which saw vast expanses of chalk laid down in shallow tropical seas. During most of the Jurassic and Cretaceous Periods, Cornwall plus much of Devon formed a large island – '**The Cornubian Island**'.

The Mesozoic was the time when the dinosaurs were the dominant creatures on land; remains of these and other life-forms found elsewhere in Britain can give us some idea of what creatures and plants would have inhabited the Cornubian Island. However, we first return to the aftermath of the Variscan Orogeny to pick up the story and describe the final period of the Palaeozoic – the Permian.

The Permian

During the **Permian**, Britain lay in the centre of a large land-mass, about 15° north of the Equator, with a hot, semi-arid climate. Cornwall would perhaps have resembled the mountainous region of the Sinai Peninsula in Egypt today, or the mountains of northern Chile. At their full height, the Variscan mountains were probably of sufficient altitude to cause a wetter climate to develop above a certain level. Perhaps, just as in present-day deserts, there were long periods without rain, interrupted by occasional violent storms which caused torrential flash-floods and mudflows, when huge volumes of loose material including large boulders were moved downslope and deposited as alluvial sediments.

Fortunately, a tiny patch of such sediment is found underlying the Permian lava at Kingsand (on the beach, 1 km northeast of the village), which can tell us much about the environment at that time (*Figure 73a*). The sediments include sandstones and coarse breccias with boulders of lava and other rocks up to 1 m across, together with finer-grained pale-coloured sediments immediately underlying the lava, which may represent some form of altered volcanic ash.

Most intriguing of all, there are animal burrows similar to those already known in

Figure 73

a (above) Permian breccia at Kingsand: note the large boulder 0.5 m across below the bag. This breccia represents debris brought down by occasional storms from the Variscan mountains at about the time that the granites were being intruded

b (below) Beaconites *burrows in Permian sediments at Kingsand. We know very little about the organism which made these burrows – was it an amphibian or a primitive reptile, a giant worm, or what?*

Torbay and usually considered to have been dug by an unknown organism called *Beaconites* (*Figure 73b*). Learned papers have debated whether this was a worm, an amphibian, or some form of primitive, perhaps limbless, burrowing reptile; this was before the dinosaurs had developed. Perhaps the climate was so hot that the poor creature had to dig burrows to avoid the heat of the day. Creatures, of course, imply that there was something for them to live on, so there must have been some plants.

Where the red sediments rest on the underlying Staddon Grits of Devonian age, the older rocks have been deeply stained red to produce some wonderful variegated patterns. This is Permian desert weathering.

To the south of Cornwall, the extensional faulting referred to at the end of Chapter 7 had caused great basins to develop; the Plymouth Bay Basin is filled with a thickness of nearly 10 km of sediments, derived from the erosion of the Variscan mountain range. Some of the younger sediments in this basin are probably of Triassic age, which marks the transition into the Mesozoic. Fishermen operating in the waters south of Cornwall know that there are several areas where there are crags and boulders of red sandstone, which they sometimes pick up in their nets.

The Triassic

In South-west England both the Permian and Triassic sediments were laid down under similar desert conditions and are together known as the 'New Red Sandstone'. Sediments of Triassic age are found in east Devon, where the base of the Triassic is marked by a conglomerate known as the Budleigh Salterton Pebble Beds. The well-rounded cobbles and pebbles making up the Pebble Beds probably mark the course of a large river flowing northwards. The pebbles are mainly of quartzite similar to the Ordovician quartzites found in the Roseland Breccia Formation. Was there a range of hills made of this quartzite in the area now occupied by the English Channel? Or did it really come from the far side of the channel, in Normandy or Brittany?

The erosion of the Variscan mountains continued through the Triassic and, with the cross-course mineralisation taking place at depth, there were probably hot springs of some kind at the surface. In Somerset and further north, shallow basins developed towards the end of the Triassic, in which mud and wind-blown dust accumulated, to form what is now known as the Mercia Mudstone Formation. In places, temporary lakes and arms of the sea dried up, producing beds of salt, exploited nowadays to provide the grit which helps to keep the roads in winter free of ice. The faint red smear we get on our windscreens when a lot of salt has been used on the road is a relic of that dust blown into the dried-up lakes of the Triassic.

After 80 million years of a desert climate, towards the end of the Triassic it began to become wetter, and the sea started to invade the area around Cornwall again. By the time the Jurassic Period commenced the sea had covered much of east Devon, Somerset, Gloucestershire and Dorset, and the Cornubian Island was surrounded by seas, a situation which persisted throughout most of the Jurassic and Cretaceous.

The Cornubian Island during the Mesozoic

It would not have been a particularly large island, probably just over 200 km long, about the size of present-day Jamaica and with a similar climate; for Cornwall still lay a long way south of its present position, and the whole planet was a great deal warmer. Atmospheric carbon dioxide levels were somewhat higher than at present, so that the

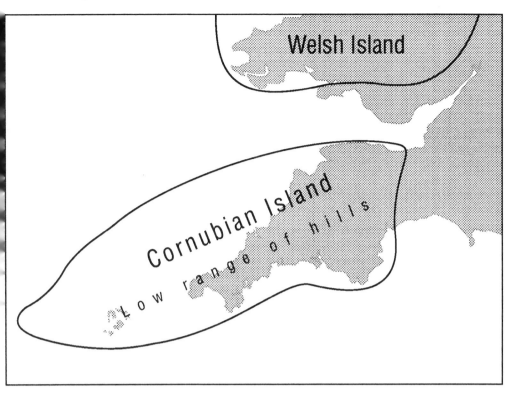

Figure 74 *Sketch map showing the approximate extent of the Cornubian Island in the Jurassic Period.*

planet was in what we would call nowadays a 'greenhouse' condition, although oxygen was sufficiently abundant for land animals to thrive.

The island would have included all of Cornwall and most of south, central and north Devon. At times, the island would have probably extended much farther west than the present Land's End (*Figure 74*).

The Variscan mountains had probably been reduced by erosion to form a range of gentle hills by the beginning of the Mesozoic. Rocks of **Jurassic** age have been found in petroleum exploration boreholes sunk offshore to the north and south of Cornwall; these have shown that the Jurassic sediments offshore are mainly limestones and mudrocks, with little evidence of the sort of coarse sediment deposition that one would expect if the Cornubian Island had been mountainous and undergoing rapid erosion.

The vegetation on the island would have included ferns, conifers and cycads; broad-leaved trees and grasses were yet to make their appearance. If the terrain was fairly flat and the climate humid, extensive swamps would probably have developed (*Figure 66* – Jurassic-Palaeogene). In these swamps and on the surrounding hills there was probably a plentiful fauna of dinosaurs. A reconstruction of the life around a Jurassic pond in the Cotswolds has been created (*Figure 75*), based on extensive fossil evidence, by Dr Michael Benton of Bristol University and artist Pamela Baldaro; this is probably as good an indication of the types of animal which would have roamed the Cornubian Island as it is possible to obtain.

Figure 75 *Reconstruction of a Jurassic scene in Gloucestershire about 165 Ma. This is one of the nearest fossil localities where we can glimpse what kind of life may have inhabited the Cornubian Island. The animals are grouped around a pond, in which their bones would be subsequently preserved as fossils. A painting by Pam Baldaro, reproduced with permission.*

Key to the various animals involved

1	*Lepidotus* sp., fish	6	"Ceratosaur" theropod
2	Discoglossid frog	7	"Fabrosaurid" ornithopod
3	*?Marmorerpeton* sp (salamander)	8	Stegosaur
4	"Goniopholid" crocodile	9	*Stereognathus ooliticus*
5	Rhamphorhyncid pterosaurs (flying reptiles)	10	Docodont mammal

The picture also shows the weathered bones of *Cetiosaurus* in the pond, centre.

Elsewhere in the world deep chemical weathering is characteristic of the Jurassic, and this deep weathering, penetrating along major zones of weakness in the granites and other older rocks, began to create the Cornish landscape (*Figure 86* – top). Deep weathering also affected the lodes, particularly those rich in sulphides of copper (*Figure 69*). Copper was completely leached from near the surface, leaving an iron-rich 'gossan'. Leaching affected the zone below, as well, so it too was poor in copper values. Deeper still the miners found a 'zone of secondary enrichment', where the copper leached from near the surface had been precipitated, which gave way in depth to the primary ore. The ore in the zone of secondary enrichment was richer than the primary lode, and this often enabled a mine to become established and financially viable.

In mid-Jurassic times there were some quite important earth movements, which are known to have produced extensive faulting in the areas to the east such as in Dorset. Probably this episode of faulting also affected the Cornubian Island, but it is almost impossible to determine which faults are of this age.

In the earliest part of the **Cretaceous Period**, conditions appear to have been rather similar to those in the Jurassic, with a coastline which was, at times, far out from the present shore of Cornwall. Dry land would have extended west of the Isles of Scilly, and Newfoundland would have been about 500 km further to the west.

The North Atlantic Ocean, as we know it today, did not exist in the Jurassic and Early Cretaceous. The southern part of the North Atlantic (between Spain and the eastern seaboard of the United States) had already begun to open up in the early Mesozoic, but the rift between South-west England/southern Ireland and Newfoundland did not start to open until the mid-Cretaceous.

Initially the crust was stretched along the line of the break, which was about 300 km west of the Isles of Scilly, causing it to become thin and eventually to break apart. To begin with, the faulting would probably have formed a rift valley something like those in present-day East Africa – geologists call this feature 'the 'Rockall rift'. Then, the two sides of the rift began to move apart as new oceanic crust was produced at the mid-ocean spreading axis and the sea flooded into the newly born ocean. Initially it must have looked like the present day Red Sea but, as the ocean widened, great blocks of crust at the continental margin foundered and were faulted down into the deep water to the west. The North Atlantic has been getting wider ever since, as new oceanic crust is produced at the spreading axis in the huge volcanic ridge (the Mid-Atlantic Ridge) that runs down the centre of the ocean. There is also evidence that the whole of the south-west peninsula has been gently tilting towards the west ever since, with the result that the Isles of Scilly would have stood much higher in relation to Dartmoor in Mesozoic times. This tilt was perhaps due, in part, to the weight of sediments laid down on the continental shelf.

One effect of these tectonic plate movements was to cause a limited outbreak of volcanicity close to Cornwall. The Wolf Rock, a small islet no more than 60 m across in the English Channel nine miles southwest of Land's End, is probably the eroded stump of a mid-Cretaceous volcano which erupted a type of lava known as phonolite. The nearby sub-sea Epson Shoal is composed of similar lava which was erupted slightly earlier.

The Atlantic Ocean widened rapidly in the Cretaceous, due to an unusually high rate of oceanic-crust production at the mid-ocean spreading axis. This coincided with a rapid rise in sea levels world-wide. As a result, the Cornubian Island became progressively submerged by the sea in which chalk was being deposited. Perhaps the highest areas of Bodmin Moor and some of the other granites remained above sea level as small islands; erosion surfaces at 300 m and 200 m on Bodmin Moor have been suggested to be of marine origin and are more likely to have been formed in the Late Cretaceous than at any later time. Sandy beaches would have fringed the tropical isles in the Upper Cretaceous sea but, away from the shallow water, **chalk** would have been deposited. Chalk is a limestone largely composed of microscopic 'coccoliths', which are the remains of blue-green algae which bloomed in the Cretaceous sea; organisms with siliceous skeletons provided the silica to create the flints, which commonly occur as nodules in most layers of chalk. The lower-lying parts of Cornwall would probably have been mantled by a white layer of chalk with flints by the end of the Campanian Stage of the Cretaceous (*Figure 76a,* in the next chapter).

Towards the end of the Cretaceous Period, during the Maastrictian Stage, the sea level fell again and much of the recently deposited chalk would have been washed away, leaving behind a scatter of the harder flints. Even today, on the south coast of Cornwall, large accumulations of flint are found making up the beaches, such as at Loe Bar and Charlestown; these are part of the evidence for the former existence of a cover of chalk. A flint gravel was found during the construction of the Marazion by-pass, underlain by a sand, which may just possibly be the remains of a Cretaceous beach sand, still in the position where it was formed.

As the sea level fell, the land-mass we know as Cornwall began to take form, and rivers developed. Most of the more important rivers in Cornwall flow from north to south (Tamar, Fowey and Fal), possibly reflecting the fact that they developed on a southward-tilted surface in Late Cretaceous times (*Figure 76a*). The Tamar and Fal flow between the larger granite masses, suggesting that these were higher ground at the time of the initiation of the present drainage pattern.

At the end of the Cretaceous, 65 Ma, it would appear that a cataclysmic event occurred which wiped out the dinosaurs and many other forms of life. Many now believe that this was due to the impact in the Gulf of Mexico of an extra-terrestrial body, a meteorite or something similar, but there is increasing evidence that many of the dominant life forms of the Mesozoic were in trouble before the time of the impact event.

An impact of a large extra-terrestrial body would almost certainly have resulted in colossal tidal waves, which would have overwhelmed the shores surrounding Cornwall and rushed inland. This would have been followed by the sun being partially blotted out by the dust thrown up into the higher atmosphere. As recent volcanic events have shown, it is likely that the dust in the atmosphere would also have caused a marked deterioration in the climate, from which it may have taken decades, or even centuries, to recover.

11 *The Tertiary – halfway house to today*

Many of today's familiar life-forms became important in the Tertiary – mammals became the dominant large land animals, and broad-leaved trees and grasses became abundant. The dinosaurs had completely died out. The climate to begin with was subtropical, but it became cooler later in the Tertiary, culminating in the ice ages of the Quaternary. This brings us right up to the present day; the many subdivisions of geological time over the last 65 million years are set out in the table below (remember, oldest at the bottom, Ma = millions of years):

CENOZOIC ERA	**Quaternary Sub-era**		Holocene Epoch	
			---------------------------------------10,000 years	
			Pleistocene Epoch	
	--- 1.8 Ma			
	Tertiary Sub-era	Neogene Period	Pliocene Epoch	
			-------------------------------------- 5.2 Ma	
			Miocene Epoch	
		--- 23.3 Ma		
		Palaeogene Period	Oligocene Epoch	
			-------------------------------------- 34.0 Ma	
			Eocene Epoch	
			------------------------------------- 56.5 Ma	
			Palaeocene Epoch	
--- 65.0 Ma				
MESOZOIC ERA		Cretaceous Period		

Palaeogene

At the beginning of the **Palaeogene Period**, the sea seems to have withdrawn so that it was confined to narrow arms in the centres of the English Channel and the Irish Sea. Volcanic activity on a massive scale occurred along the west coast of Scotland and in Northern Ireland, triggered by the plate movements associated with the final stage in the opening of the North Atlantic between Greenland and Scotland. Lundy, in the Bristol Channel, was an outlying manifestation of this volcanicity; the granite which now forms the island is but part of a once-larger volcanic centre, now reduced by Atlantic storms to lie mainly beneath the waves. Eruptions of the Lundy volcano would have been visible from north Cornwall and northerly winds could have brought a dusting of volcanic ash onto the Cornish landscape in early Palaeogene times.

Cornwall would probably have been a hilly area with fairly gentle relief during the **Palaeocene**, with a climate warmer than today (*Figure 76b*). Climatic conditions may have favoured a special type of weathering which led to the precipitation of silica in the

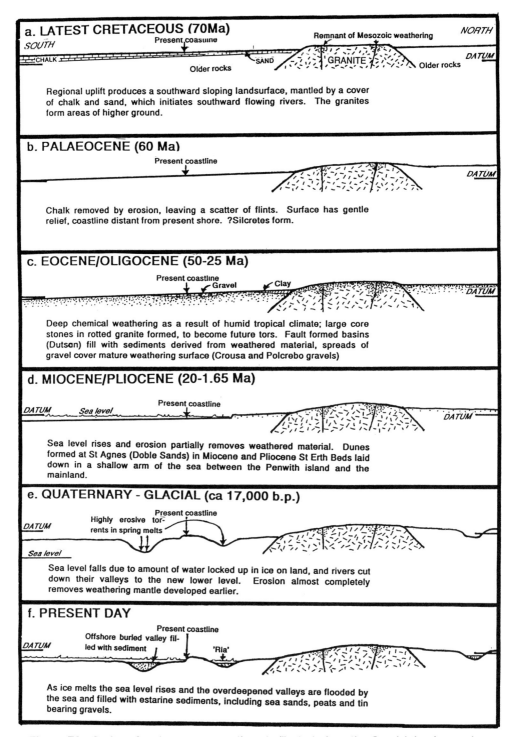

Figure 76 *Series of cartoon cross-sections to illustrate how the Cornish landscape has evolved from the Late Cretaceous to the present day.*

weathering profile, to form a hard rock known as 'silcrete'. The most famous examples of silcrete are the sarsen stones of Salisbury Plain, used in the construction of Stonehenge. Recent excavations for a wind farm on St Breock Downs showed that the hard silicified boulders littering the surface were underlain by soft, deeply weathered Staddon Grits, thereby raising the possibility that these boulders are a form of silcrete, maybe of Palaeocene age. Large boulders of silcrete-like quartz are found in the Kea-Baldhu-Carnon area (see the waterfall feature in Carnon Downs Garden Centre) and may represent another area of silcrete boulders in south Cornwall. Many early writers (notably Rev. Whitley in the *Transactions of the Royal Cornwall Geological Society* for 1910, who reported that the rockeries in Victoria Gardens came from the Kea-Baldhu area) commented on the abundance of large quartz boulders littering the landscape in many parts of Cornwall, and reported that these were the main source of material for road construction in the 19th century and had nearly all been removed by the end of the century.

In the early **Eocene** the climate became tropical, with a mean annual temperature of around 25°C (*Figure 76c*). This temperature has been deduced from a study of the well-preserved flora of the Eocene London Clay. Sediments of Eocene age, which have been dated by the spores they contain, are found just north of Launceston where a small fault-defined basin about 1 km^2 in area occurs at Dutson, just on the Cornish side of the Tamar. The beds include sands, sandy clays and lignitic clays and closely resemble the beds of Eocene/Oligocene age found in the much larger Bovey and Petrockstow Basins in Devon and the even-larger Stanley Banks Basin under the waters of the Bristol Channel east of Lundy. Re-activation of strike-slip faults seems to have been the principal mechanism which led to the creation of these basins, which then acted as receptacles for sediment derived from the soft weathering mantle washed in from the area around the basin. Ball clays from the Devon basins are an important commercial product for use in ceramics. A clay pit was briefly operated in the 1920s at Dutson to exploit the clays for brick manufacture.

Similar clays are found south of St Agnes Beacon, around Beacon Cottage, although there are no exposures where these clays can be seen today. Studies of the spores contained in these clays indicate they are of **Oligocene** age. This clay had the unusual property of being able to stick candles onto miners' caps, hence it is known as the 'candle clay'.

Before moving on, we should look at some curious patches of gravel in west Cornwall, at Crousa in the Lizard near St Keverne, and at Polcrebo, on the western side of the Carnmenellis granite (*Figure 76c*). Spores and pollen found in the Crousa Gravels suggest they are of Palaeogene age. Also, all the igneous and slate fragments in these gravels have been deeply rotted in a way reminiscent of the intense chemical weathering which characterises the Eocene and Oligocene elsewhere, so it has been assumed that these beds are of Eocene age. Similar gravels, which can be rather more securely dated to the Eocene, occur on top of the Haldon Hills near Exeter. At the present time there is no convenient location where the Polcrebo gravels can be seen, but St Keverne Parish Council have made a small picnic area around the old gravel pit on Crousa Down in the Lizard, where these enigmatic gravels can be inspected.

The surface on which the Polcrebo and Crousa gravels and the St Agnes candle clay rest probably forms part of an ancient gently sloping plain (*Figure 76c, 77*). If one looks out across any non-granite area in Cornwall west of the Bodmin granite, one sees

Figure 77 *St Agnes Beacon, north of Porthtowan. Is this an old island above the Tertiary sea or was it formed as an inselberg? See text for details*

a flat surface composed of the plateau-like tops of many hills. This **killas plateau** is now dissected by valleys, but originally was part of a gently undulating plain that sloped gradually to a shoreline a considerable distance out from the present coast (*Figure 85,* in Chapter 13). This kind of surface is the product of a long period of erosion which has reduced the hills to a plain, and is known to geomorphologists as a *planation surface*. In west Cornwall this surface is known as the Reskajeage Surface.

If one looks towards St Agnes from the A30 at Carland Cross wind farm, one sees that St Agnes Beacon forms a raised hump which looks as if it might have once been an island. Some believe that this is exactly what it was, during a period of high sea level in the Miocene or Pliocene, though others suggest that long periods of erosion can produce steep-sided hills like this, known as 'inselbergs'. Other areas of high ground, such as the Carnmenellis and Land's End granites, are bordered by steep slopes and may have had a similar origin as inselberg-like features.

The eastern part of Cornwall is less easy to understand from a geomorphological point of view; generally the land stands at a higher level and there are no little patches of Tertiary beds resting on the surface. The dividing line between the two areas is our old friend the Start-Perranporth Line, and it may be that there was fault movement along this line in mid-Tertiary times, which had the effect of lowering the western part of the county by 100 m or thereabouts.

The fault movements which formed the Dutson Basin near Launceston must have had an effect on the surface of the time, certainly the course of the River Tamar seems generally to follow NW-SE faults (the Tamar Valley Fault Zone) for much of its length. However, the incised meanders of the River Tamar between Greystone Bridge and Gunnislake indicate that the river must, at some stage, have been meandering in a mature valley of gentle relief, before a fall in sea level caused the river to cut its bed lower, resulting in the meanders becoming incised.

Neogene

The **Neogene Period** in the British Isles is generally poorly represented, but Cornwall is lucky to have small patches of both Miocene and Pliocene sediments. The **Miocene** is represented by red sands and clays which lie on the northern slopes of St Agnes Beacon and are exposed in a series of small sand and clay pits (*Figure 76d*). Spores

Figure 78 *Historic picture of the St Erth sand pit in operation (circa 1900-1910). These late Pliocene beds were laid down in a shallow arm of the sea just before the onset of the Quaternary glaciations. Abundant fossils, notably gastropods (Figure 18h) indicate a Mediterranean climate. The sand was used as a foundry moulding sand and was probably an important factor in the success of Harvey's foundry at Hayle (photograph courtesy of the Royal Cornwall Museum).*

and pollen indicate there was a Mediterranean climate including conifers, mixed woodland and heathland plants. The grains of sand appear to have been wind-blown and the clay layers may represent deposition in the wetter hollows between dunes. Perhaps we are dealing with a dune belt just inland from the shoreline, which would seem to indicate a sea level rather higher than at present. The sands and clays have been exploited in a small way for specialised uses connected with iron-founding by the Doble family for several generations, and in recognition of this fact the formation is known as the 'Doble Sands'.

Small patches of clayey sand up to 7 m thick occur near St Erth and are known as the St Erth Beds; they are believed to be of late **Pliocene** age (*Figure 76d*). They were first-class foundry moulding sands which were exploited in the past (*Figure 78*) for use by the Hayle foundry and nowadays form an important Site of Special Scientific Interest (SSSI). Many beautifully preserved fossils were obtained from the sand pits, including a rich fauna of gastropods and other shellfish (*Figure 18h*). These indicate that the St Erth Beds were laid down in a shallow arm of the sea with a sea temperature comparable to the present day Mediterranean. The St Erth Beds now lie at an elevation of 30-37 m, and are believed to have been laid down in a sea no deeper than 10 m; so this suggests a sea level 40-50 m higher than present in late Pliocene times. Both the Doble Sands and the St Erth Beds indicate a high sea level; this is only to be expected, as the present day sea level is at a lower level because of the amount of water locked up in the Antarctic and Greenland ice caps. It is estimated that if these ice caps were to melt, and the worlds' oceans warm by a few degrees, that sea levels would rise around 70-90 m. Although there was probably some polar ice in the Miocene and Pliocene, it only involved a small proportion of the volume locked up in the present-day ice caps, so sea levels 40-50 m higher than at present in the Miocene and Pliocene would seem reasonable.

12 The Quaternary – the ice ages without glaciers

From a peak in temperatures during the Eocene, the climate of the Tertiary became cooler as time went on. Starting about 1.5 million years ago, there was a further marked cooling of the climate and the **Quaternary ice ages** began. The ice ages consisted of colder periods, usually known as *glacials*, and more temperate periods known as *interglacials*. Brief periods of warmer climate during the main glacials are known as *interstadials*.

Three main glacials are recognised, but there were many earlier cold periods, most of which probably did not involve a widespread development of land ice in the British Isles.

What caused 'the ice ages'?

In recent years there has been a great deal of climatological research to try and discover how the world's climate is controlled by natural forces and how the man-made outputs of gases such as carbon dioxide and methane are likely to affect the climate in the future. Oxygen-isotope studies of oceanic sediments and deep boreholes through the Greenland ice cap have provided particularly useful information about past climates.

There are many theories concerning the reason for the cooling in the late Tertiary leading to the ice ages of the Quaternary; one of the most popular at the moment is that the collision of India with the southern margin of Asia threw up the large high-altitude Tibetan plateau, which so modified the world's climate as to cause global cooling.

Natural periodicities of the earth's climate are thought to be caused by fluctuations in the in-coming solar radiation, due to astronomical factors. The resulting variation in radiation reaching the planet's surface is known as the Milankovitch solar radiation curve. The deposition of many rhythmic sedimentary sequences has been attributed to this effect, which is referred to as '*orbital forcing*'. Perhaps the rhythmic alternation of Upper Devonian slate and limestone at Marble Cliff, near Padstow (*Figure 31,* page 50), could be due to orbital forcing.

During the Quaternary, the overall cooling of the planet meant that glaciers extended as far south as London during the periods of lowest solar radiation on the Milankovitch curve, with the temperate interglacials corresponding to the periods of higher solar radiation. One of the most important discoveries in recent years has been that the interglacials are much shorter (10,000-15,000 years) than the glacial periods (up to 90,000 years), so the *normal* climate over the last million years has been much colder than present. At present, we appear to be nearing the end of the present interglacial. Interglacials tend to have a more stable climate than glacials; the last 10,000 years has been a period of unusual climatic stability. Some of the climatic changes in the previous 100,000 years, as recorded in the Greenland ice cap cores, have been of frightening rapidity, such as a 10°C change in overall temperature in Northern Europe, warming or cooling, in 10-100 years!

Figure 79   *Sandrock at Godrevy Point.   This represents a beach formed at a time of higher sea level, probably in the penultimate interglacial.   Because of its high calcium-carbonate content (from broken-up shells, etc.), it has become cemented to form a sandrock.   Sandrocks from Fistral and Padstow have been used in local church construction.*

Cornwall during the Quaternary

During the glacial periods, places like Liverpool, Leeds, Edinburgh and Glasgow would have been buried beneath ice sheets perhaps hundreds of metres thick at the peak of the glaciation, but in Cornwall we would simply have experienced extremely cold weather, partly brought about by the Gulf Stream ceasing to flow during the coldest periods. Vegetation in Cornwall during a glacial would have been a sparse tundra, similar to that today in northern Siberia.

At the peak of each glaciation the soil would have been permanently frozen to a depth of many metres and, in the coldest periods, only a shallow surface layer would have thawed in the summer.   There would have been increased runoff because of the inability of the permanently frozen ground to accept percolating water.   Ice grew in the frozen soil and the underlying weathered material and, during periods of thaw, the

129

whole mass of mud and ice could flow downslope, even on shallow slopes. This process is known as *gelifluction* and the material so formed is referred to in Cornwall as **head**. The greatest thicknesses of head tend to be found at the foot of northward-facing slopes, where up to 10 m may be found, and the material we see dug out of service trenches in Cornish roads is normally head. Head is highly variable and may be anything from a structureless clay to a material largely composed of stones which have travelled downslope. The colour of head is usually a pale brown or brownish orange. Many cliffs around Cornwall show head overlying the solid rock at the top of the cliff face.

During the glaciations there also appears to have been much wind-blown dust (= **loess**) which forms a layer up to one metre thick in places; it is well seen in parts of the Lizard and on the Isles of Scilly, although to the untutored eye it is often difficult to tell the difference between loess and some types of head.

When the ice was at its maximum extent during the last (Devensian) glaciation, there is evidence that a tongue of ice moving down from the Irish Sea reached the Isles of Scilly. The clearest example of a till laid down by glacier ice is on the northern part of St Martin's (Isles of Scilly). This till, debris left behind by a glacier, contains rock fragments up to boulder size (known as glacial erratics) of Irish Sea derivation. Carbon-14 dating suggests that this till was laid down in the final stage of the last glaciation, less than 20,000 years ago. At Trebetherick Point, at the mouth of the Camel estuary, there are boulder beds which are interpreted to have been rafted into place by river ice.

One curious feature on the shore platform just northwest of Porthleven is a large boulder of garnetiferous gneiss, known as the 'Giant's Rock', unlike anything seen on land in Cornwall. It has been postulated that this is a glacial erratic which reached its present position by being carried on an ice raft. This is rather puzzling, as the iceberg carrying the boulder would have had to be beached onshore with a sea level considerably higher than present, and high sea levels are supposed to correlate with *warm* interglacials. Evidence of extensive ice rafting at a time of high sea level is now accumulating from other locations, and there is a vigorous debate over the cause – possibly a sudden collapse of one of the great ice caps. Other supposed glacial erratics are seen at Godrevy Point and Fistral Bay.

About 190,000 years ago, during the penultimate (last-but-one) interglacial, the climate appears to have been somewhat warmer and the sea was several metres higher. Sandy beaches with a high content of shell material formed and became cemented by the calcium carbonate they contained to form a **sandrock**, now several metres above the contemporary beach. This is well seen at Godrevy Point, near Hayle (*Figure 79*), and also on the north side of Fistral Bay; at both localities the sandrock is overlain by head formed in a later cold period. Sandrocks from Fistral and Padstow have been used in the construction of some of the churches in their vicinities, notably at Crantock, partly because they were easy to cut (*Figure 24h*). There is some evidence that there are two cycles of raised-beach formation at Fistral, with the youngest phase being formed in the last interglacial.

Raised beaches are also known at various levels from 5 m to 20 m above present sea level and possibly as high as 30 m. The lower raised beaches commonly have deposits of cobbles, gravel and sand on the platform which formed the old beach. A cliff line behind the beach platform may also have developed. In general, the highest beaches are the most degraded and appear to be the oldest. A particularly clear example of a raised beach (5-8 m) is seen west of Spit Point which is on the coast south of Par Harbour. Sands and gravels composed of well-rounded quartz pebbles are here seen forming a beach, resting on Devonian slate. Another raised beach occurs at the back of Pendower Beach, where the basal layers of sand and gravel are cemented by iron oxides (*Figure 17*); this has been dated to approximately 200,000 years ago. One of the best examples of a raised-beach platform is the shelf on which the road from Newlyn to Mousehole runs. The platform, at around 75-125 m on the northern side of the Land's End granite, was often referred to in the older literature as a raised beach, but it is now thought to be more likely to be a land planation surface, backed by an upstanding inselberg-like mass of granite (see page 126).

One of the effects of the glaciations was to lower the sea level by up to 120 m, due to the amount of water locked up in ice on land; the rivers then cut their valleys deeper to the new lower base level (*Figure 76e*). At places like Fowey and Looe, we can imagine the river flowing at the bottom of a deep narrow valley about 40-50 m below the present level of the quays. The river would have frozen up each winter, but in the spring thaw huge volumes of water, no doubt full of muddy debris, would have rushed down the valley, giving it huge erosive capacity. Drowned cliff-lines have been identified a considerable distance offshore, indicating coastlines which formed during periods of low sea level.

At the end of each glaciation, as the great masses of ice on land melted, sea level rose and the overdeepened valleys were flooded, forming 'rias' (*Figure 76f*). There is increasing evidence that rapid and catastrophic collapses in ice caps have repeatedly occurred, which would have caused a sudden and dramatic rise in sea level. Such an event may have given rise to the legend of 'The lost land of Lyonesse'.

In many cases the overdeepened valleys were filled with sediments brought down by the rivers, and they reflect a constant battle between land and sea – sometimes sea sands, sometimes peats, sometimes estuarine clays, and so on. Quite possibly the valleys were filled with sediments during an interglacial, only for them to be washed out again during the next glacial. In most of these sequences the basal layer is a coarse, poorly sorted gravel, laid down in a spring thaw in the closing stages of a glacial. This gravel often contains substantial quantities of tin; the stream tinners knew this and even went to the extent of working it below sea level and, ultimately, mining it underground in places like Restronguet Creek, Par and Pentewan, because the tin values were so high.

Prehistoric human activity was represented in these valley infillings, notably in the Wheal Virgin and Happy Union stream tin works at Pentewan, by sharpened stakes, perhaps to form some kind of wharf. The skeleton of a whale, parts of which are in the Cornwall Geological Museum in Penzance, was also found 12 m below the surface at Pentewan, together with the remains of deer and a human skull. Human activity in Britain, as represented by Palaeolithic hand axes, dates back to a time considerably before the last interglacial, so early hunters may have witnessed some of the events we are describing.

The erosive power of the spring thaws removed a high proportion of the thick layers of weathered material which had accumulated on land during the Tertiary, and these were swept away down the valleys. In the higher reaches of those rivers and streams that drained mineralised ground, the heavier minerals such as cassiterite tended to accumulate in the sandy sediments under the valley bottoms, whilst the lighter minerals

Figure 80 *Submerged forest in Mount's Bay. One of the finest occasions when the fossil forest was exposed was in 1883, when this photograph was taken. Oak, alder, hazel and birch were identified; a sample of wood from near Long Rock has been carbon-dated to just over 2000 B.C. (photograph courtesy Royal Cornwall Museum).*

such as quartz, feldspar and mica were swept on down the river. These sediments were up to 15 m thick under Goss Moor, and in places several cycles of deposition were found with a rich tin-bearing sand resting on a 'shelf' of peat or clay, which was underlain by another sand bed, at the bottom of which was another tin bearing sand or gravel.

Until the 18th century nearly all the tin produced in Cornwall came from alluvial deposits, with an estimated 40% coming from these stream-tin deposits. Joseph Collins, the great Cornish geologist and mining engineer, was involved in the final

Figure 81 *View from St Martin's Bay towards Tresco, Isles of Scilly. This was all dry land less than 2000 years ago. In Roman times these isles may have been joined as a single island.*

phase of working on Goss Moor and other adjoining areas in the early part of this century, using steam-driven suction and bucket-ladder dredges. The resulting wilderness left after this phase of working has now become of exceptional biological interest – Goss Moor is an SSSI and Redmoor and Breney Common are nature reserves belonging to Cornwall Wildlife Trust.

Between 8000 and 5000 B.C., the sea level rose rapidly in response to glacial melting, averaging some 25 mm a year. Such a rate would have been obvious to shore-dwelling human groups at the time, as on a flat coastline they would have had to move their habitations inland from time to time.

In the period from approximately 5000 to 2000 B.C., Cornwall seems to have been surrounded by a coastal plain offshore from the present line of cliffs, with a shoreline probably in the form of a beach backed by a line of dunes. On this plain grew a luxuriant forest of oak, hazel, birch and alder. As the sea level continued to rise, this forest was submerged beneath the dunes and then covered in a protective layer of beach sand. Every now and then, as current and tide dictate, a storm will strip off the layer of sand and the submerged forest is exposed to view. The most famous example of a submerged forest is in Mount's Bay (*Figure 80*, taken in 1883), which reminds us of the ancient Cornish name for St Michael's Mount – *Carrek Los yn Cos* – 'the hoar rock in the wood'. Other submerged forests are found in the Hayle Estuary, beneath the Doom Bar at the mouth of the Camel, Porthleven, Portreath, Perranporth, the Helford River, Restronguet Creek, Portmellon, Fowey and Looe.

Sea level in the area of the Isles of Scilly has been rising at a particularly high rate during historic times (4 mm per annum). So there would have been a single *Isle* of Scilly in Roman times, when it is believed that all the islands except St Agnes were joined by a central fertile plain (*Figure 81*). The shallow waters between the isles show submerged stone field boundaries and hut circles, as Charles Thomas has described in detail in his book *Exploration of a Drowned Landscape* (1985).

The rate of global sea-level rise has slowed down in historic times, although it is still continuing to rise slowly today. There is some evidence that the rate of rise is now slightly more rapid, due to global warming from human activities.

With the rise in sea level over the last 8000 years, the beach sands have gradually been driven onshore, particularly on the north coast, which faces the prevailing winds. This has caused great accumulations of wind-blown sand to develop, which have formed belts of dunes, as at Hayle Towans and Perran Sands. Smaller accumulations of similar sand are seen at Gunwalloe, Sennen, Holywell Bay and on the Rock side of the Camel estuary. Much of the sand has been formed from the broken up shells of marine organisms, so has a high content of calcium carbonate. As most of the soils in Cornwall are acid, this carbonate-rich sand provided a ready means of neutralising this acidity, and was extensively exploited for this purpose. A canal was constructed inland from Bude in 1823 to enable this sand to be conveyed to the hinterland of acid Culm soils.

Most of the dunes have now become stabilised with marram grass and other vegetation. In the past wind-blown sands have overwhelmed farms and settlements; St Piran's Oratory at Perranporth, one of Cornwall's oldest churches dating from the Dark Ages, was overwhelmed in this way, as was St Enodoc beside the Camel estuary. Some of these sands have become cemented to form a 'sandrock' (see above), as can be seen in the intertidal area of Harlyn Bay.

13 The present-day scenery of Cornwall

This brings us to the present day. We have already shown how the geological history of Cornwall has contributed to the present-day scenery, so all we need to do in this final section is to review the component parts of the scenery and the way geology controls it.

The coast

The picturesque coastline of Cornwall embodies a large number of land forms, ranging from tranquil creeks to wide sandy beaches and rugged cliffs.

Rocky cliffs are the most dramatic part of Cornwall's scenery. They are under constant attack by the sea, which seeks out any line of weakness to break up the rock mass. Many of the prominent headlands are made up of relatively resistant igneous rock, either the basic igneous rocks of Devonian or Carboniferous age as at Black Head (*Figure 27*), Trevose Head, Nare Head or Pentire Head; or the Variscan granites which form Land's End, Gwennap Head or Trewavas Head. Some of the harder sedimentary rocks, such as the Staddon Grits, also produce headlands, as on the west coast at Trenance Point, west of St Eval. Very hard rock masses, such as the Ordovician quartzites in the Roseland Breccia Formation, also produce striking crags in the cliffs, as can be seen behind Great Perhaver Beach, near Gorran Haven.

Where the cliffs are made of Devonian or Carboniferous sedimentary rocks, much depends on the presence of lines of weakness such as faults, and the attitude of the cleavage or bedding. If the cleavage is dipping away from the face, then the face is relatively stable (*Figure 82a*). If it is dipping towards the sea, then there will always be a tendency for blocks to detach themselves and slide down on the cleavage surfaces (*Figure 82b*), as is seen in the cliffs south of Ropehaven, on the west side of St Austell Bay. Bedding, where prominent, will have similar effects, as can be seen in the cliffs formed from Upper Carboniferous turbidite sandstones and shales along the stretch of coastline from the Rusey Fault (*Figure 69*) north to the county boundary.

Where there are strong vertical joints, the cliff face can fail by toppling of the blocks (*Figure 82c*). Wedge failures occur where there is a block isolated by joints which intersect behind the face (*Figure 82d*). Where the material making up the cliff is relatively weak, as for example where it is weathered, then a rotational failure can take place (*Figure 82e*), often triggered by the presence of water under pressure in the zone of the slip plane. Rotational failures can occur, although they are much commoner in the softer rocks of east Devon and Dorset. Sometimes a massive sea cave can be formed, which collapses; a combination of a sea-cave collapse leading to a massive rotational failure gave rise to Lawarnick Pit, on the north side of Kynance Cove (*Figures 82f, 83* and on the *back cover*). Talc-rich zones in the serpentine also helped to lubricate this particular slip.

Raised beaches have already been mentioned; cliffs frequently have a notch in them corresponding to the position of a former cliff line and wave-cut platform, sometimes with the ancient beach preserved. The South West Coast Path frequently makes use of a ledge caused by the presence of a raised beach, as on the east side of Par Sands.

134

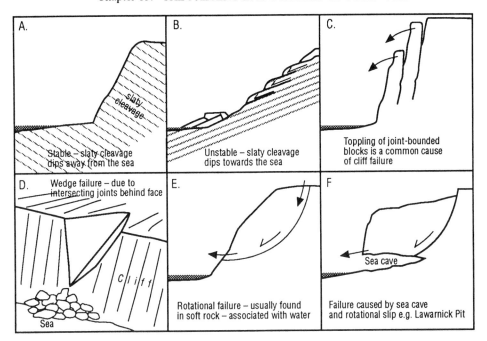

Figure 82 *A series of diagrams to show how different types of cliff failure can occur in Cornwall.*

Figure 83 *Lawarnick Pit, Kynance Cove. This 'pit' looks rather like a large quarry, but was the site of a massive cliff failure, triggered by the collapse of a sea cave (see also the explanation inside the back cover).*

The rate of cliff retreat has been a subject of much debate recently. A typical figure for a slate cliff is probably around 2 m per century, although this can rise to 5 m per century or more in low cliffs composed of weak or weathered rocks in exposed situations. The rate of cliff retreat is very spasmodic; a face may remain stable for hundreds of years, then it may fail by 10 m or more all at once.

The present line of cliffs have probably been repeatedly refashioned during each interglacial. During each period of high sea level, wave action would have eroded the cliffs back – so in theory a million years of constant cliff erosion would result in the cliffs retreating by several tens of kilometres, but erosion has not been constant and sea level has been going up and down through the Quaternary like a yo-yo, so this is a much too simplistic calculation!

Major faults with nearly vertical fault planes are exploited by the sea to give rise to sea caves, inlets and bays. Larger estuaries, such as at Looe, may also be aligned along a line of weakness caused by a fault (*Figure 84*). Mineral lodes sometimes have a zone of soft altered rock on either side of the vein, which can be exploited by the sea to create a sea cave or indentation in the coastline. Extensional normal faults (as in *Figure 11b*) can create lines of weakness down which blocks can slip, given a seaward-dipping fault plane; this is well seen in the north coast near Portreath, where east-west faults dipping northwards produce prominent facets in the upper part of the cliff.

The larger bays can be caused by the underlying rock type being slightly softer, such as the Dartmouth Slates at Watergate Bay. However, more frequently it is because the land behind was low-lying anyway, such as behind Hayle Sands, or because there has been extensive rotting of the rocks by processes associated with the mineralisation. A

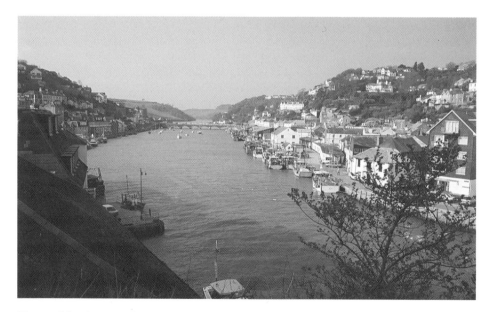

Figure 84 *Looe, a long straight valley eroded along a line of weakness, probably a fault. During the glacials the Looe river would have cut its bed well below present sea level, in response to the lowered sea level during glacial times caused by the amount of water locked up in ice on the land.*

good example of the latter would be Perranporth Sands, where the slates have been extensively altered by processes associated with the Start-Perranporth Line. In the case of St Austell Bay, the land behind the bay was already low-lying and the rocks have been extensively altered by circulating fluids arising from the St Austell granite.

We have already referred to the extensive accumulations of sand driven onto the west-facing beaches of the north coast, particularly at Perran Sands and Hayle Towans. Nowadays these dune fields are no longer mobile, and have been stabilised by marram grass being planted. Because of the high calcium-carbonate content of the sand, the vegetation on these dunes, and in the surrounding area affected by blown sand, is lime loving and distinctly different to the vegetation associated with the normally acid soils of Cornwall.

On the south coast there are many examples of shingle beaches, often with a high flint content. The most notable example is Loe Bar, near Helston, which has been built across the mouth of a valley developed along the line of the Carrick Thrust, and is aligned perpendicular to the main attack of Atlantic storms.

The estuaries

As has already been suggested, many of the more important estuaries are aligned, at least in part, along faults (*Figure 84*). The older Variscan thrust faults do not seem to have a strong influence, although the Fal estuary and the lower part of Loe Pool may be partly aligned along the Carrick Thrust.

The most important feature of the estuaries has already been described, with the rivers having cut down their valleys in relation to lowered sea levels during the cold periods of the Quaternary, producing the flooded valleys or **rias** so typical of the south coast of Cornwall and Devon. The steep-sided valleys of the lower reaches of many of the southward-flowing rivers is an indication of the way they were rapidly cut down into the killas plateau during the periods of low sea level.

In many cases the flooded valleys have been infilled with sediments washed down the rivers, and in recent times backfilled, mostly due to tin-streaming in the upper reaches causing the rivers to carry high bed-loads. The extent of this backfilling is quite striking: Tregony was an important medieval trading port on the River Fal, but is now some miles inland from the highest point tides can reach. Pont's Mill, on the Par River, was also a port which 80-ton sea-going vessels could reach as late as 1720, but is now several miles inland. Strangely, the Fowey Estuary has not been so badly silted up, in spite of the River Fowey draining a large area of Bodmin Moor, which was extensively streamed for tin.

In the case of the rivers draining the St Austell granite, sand from china-clay working is also a contributor to this process. Beaches such as Par, Carlyon Bay (*Figure 85*) and Pentewan have all been formed from china-clay waste. The china-clay companies in recent years have stopped discharging micaceous residue into the rivers so, as the principal source of sediment is now cut off, some of these beaches are now showing signs of erosion.

The killas plateau

The killas plateau (*Figure 85*) represents a planation surface which is probably the product of a long period of weathering, starting with the intense tropical weathering of Mesozoic and early Tertiary times. These deep chemical weathering profiles have

Figure 85 *Carlyon Bay, a beach formed from sand washed down from clayworks in the Carclaze area. The level planation surface (the 'killas plateau') developed on the Devonian slates can be seen behind, sloping seawards from an elevation of approximately 120 m at Castle Dore to 60 m at Menabilly.*

mostly been swept away by erosion but, in places, pockets remain; the largest example lies under the south side of Goss Moor, where a zone of weathering 60 m deep extends from Indian Queens through Gaverigan towards Roche. This was recently spectacularly displayed in the cuttings for the Indian Queens by-pass (now grassed over).

The way in which the rivers cut down into the killas plateau during the glacial phases of the Quaternary has already been mentioned. Generally, the steep-sided over-deepened valleys are restricted to the killas; the only steep-sided valleys to traverse granite terrain are the Retew Gorge of the Fal and the Luxulyan valley, both in the St Austell granite.

The killas plateau slopes gently towards the west, with the highest areas of plateau in the northeast around Davidstow, where it reaches 280 m in altitude. Further west on St Breock Downs there is another high area, at around 210 m; as we have already seen, this appears to be capped by a scatter of silcrete blocks which may be of early Tertiary age. This suggests that in north Cornwall there may be the remains of a surface of this age, perhaps Palaeocene, which stands at a higher level than the main Reskajeage Surface further west, which is presumed to be slightly younger, of Eocene-Oligocene age.

Most of the main rivers (Fal, Fowey and Tamar) flow from north to south, possibly initiated on a southward-dipping surface of Cretaceous chalk. The incised meanders of the Tamar between Greystone and Gunnislake probably developed in a wide mature valley with a gentle gradient, in relation to a sea level higher than at present, which suggests a pre-Quaternary, perhaps Pliocene, age. The lowering of sea level through the Quaternary caused the lower reaches of the Tamar to be significantly down-cut, producing the deeply incised meanders; this was given added emphasis by the exceptionally low sea levels of the glacial periods.

The southward-flowing rivers seem to have been capable of more effective downcutting than those flowing north and in one case this caused river capture to take place. Originally the River Fal flowed westwards from its origin in Tregoss Moor, across Goss Moor and on down the Porth valley, reaching the sea just north of Newquay. However, a more vigorously downcutting river, occupying the lower reaches of the present River Fal, cut a channel through a weak zone in the St Austell granite caused by a combination of the Fal Valley fault and intense kaolinisation. This enabled the headwaters of the original Fal to be captured and flow southwards down what is now known as the Retew Gorge. The capture has probably happened in the geologically recent past, for it would only need a change in level of a few metres for the river to flow to the west again.

The granite moors

Nearly all of the granites form high areas of moorland. The highest point in Cornwall – Brown Willy (420 m) – lies in the northeastern part of the Bodmin Moor granite.

Generally speaking, the granites form gently undulating areas of upland, with the occasional rocky **tor** protruding above this surface. Tor formation is something which has long been debated in the scientific literature. Deep weathering during the Mesozoic and Tertiary penetrated along faults and major joints (*Figure 86*) to considerable depths. As the weathering worked inwards from the major joints, so cores of hard unweathered granite were isolated. Later on, perhaps during the late Tertiary or the Quaternary, the surrounding soft weathered material (called **regolith**) was eroded away, leaving the rounded rocky eminences we call 'tors' standing up above the surface (*Figure 87*).

In some cases the weathering completely isolated the cores of granite, so that when the softer regolith was washed away, **core-stones** of granite remained to lie in a jumble on the surface or on the sides of valley, as we see around Luxulyan. Occasionally a core-stone will be left balanced, so it can be rocked – this is called a **logan rock** (*Figure 87*).

Examination of stereoscopic aerial photographs shows that the 'softer' areas, notably the marshy hollows, are aligned along lineaments. The wide marshy hollows (known as 'slads'), when investigated by boreholes, are found to be underlain by greater or lesser thicknesses of decomposed granite, often with a quartz vein marking the position of the lineament deduced from the aerial photographs. In places, true kaolinised granite will be found, particularly at the intersection of lineaments. This reminds us that the final phase in the formation of the china-clay deposits was probably a form of deep chemical weathering during the Mesozoic and/or the Cenozoic.

On slopes in the granite areas during the periglacial conditions of the ice ages, movement of the soil, subsoil and underlying granite, particularly if it was soft and decomposed, produced a material which often shows streaks in it corresponding with the direction of downhill movement; this is a variety of head. Sometimes this material contained worthwhile tin values and was washed by the tin streamers to recover cassiterite. together with small quantities of gold. Many gullies on the granite moorlands owe their origin to this activity. In the northeastern part of Bodmin Moor, around Buttern Hill, it was washed for wolfram (tungsten ore).

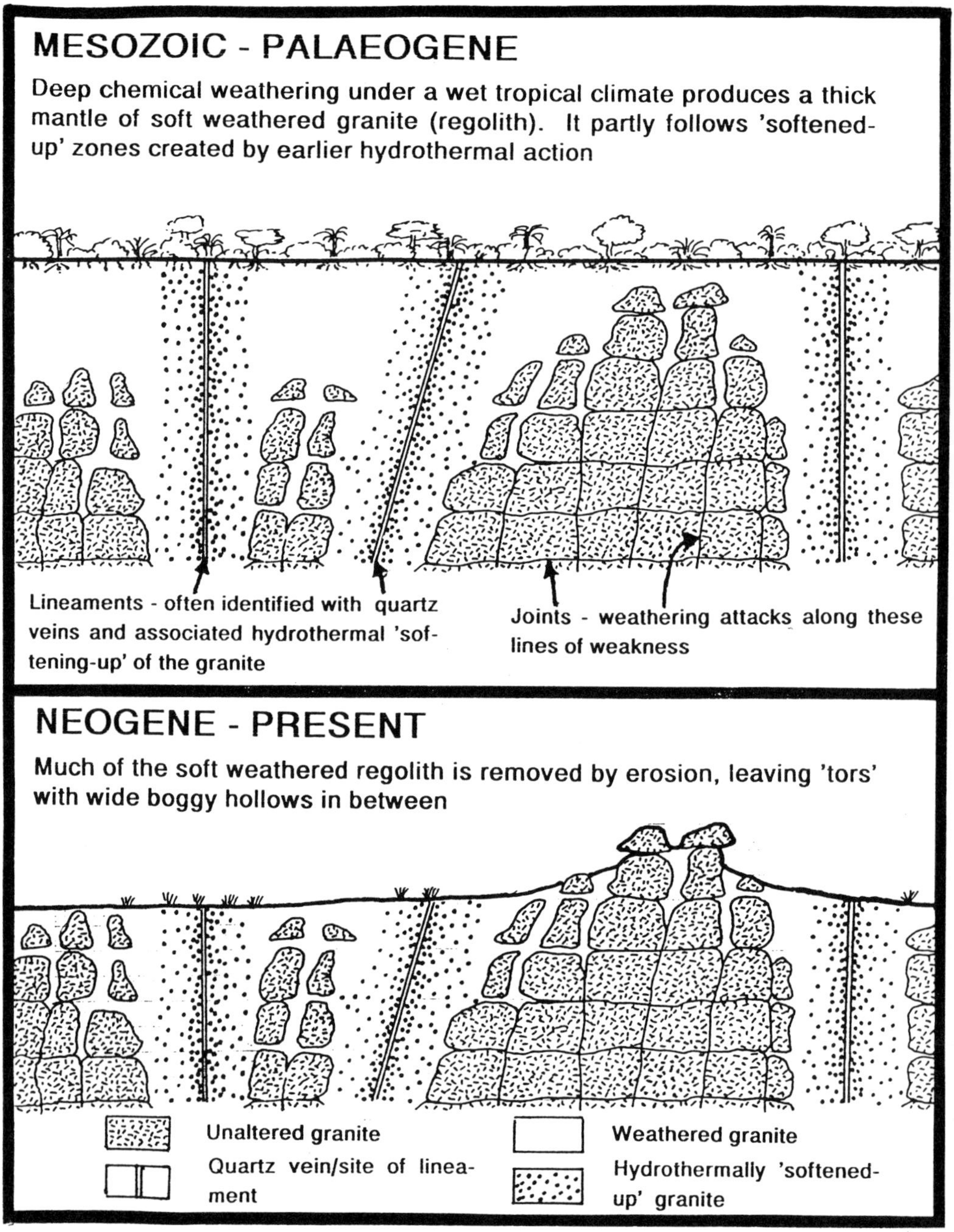

MESOZOIC - PALAEOGENE

Deep chemical weathering under a wet tropical climate produces a thick mantle of soft weathered granite (regolith). It partly follows 'softened-up' zones created by earlier hydrothermal action

Lineaments - often identified with quartz veins and associated hydrothermal 'softening-up' of the granite

Joints - weathering attacks along these lines of weakness

NEOGENE - PRESENT

Much of the soft weathered regolith is removed by erosion, leaving 'tors' with wide boggy hollows in between

Unaltered granite

Quartz vein/site of lineament

Weathered granite

Hydrothermally 'softened-up' granite

Figure 86 *Sections to illustrate how granite tors are formed.*

Figure 87 *Logan Rock on Louden Hill with Rough Tor in the background, Bodmin Moor. Weathering of granite to produce tors often leaves isolated blocks (core-stones) which can sometimes be rocked – called logan rocks.*

The wide marshy hollows are also underlain by thin superficial deposits of sand and peat, almost invariably disturbed to some extent by the activities of tin streamers. The winnowing action of streams, notably during the spring-thaw conditions of the glacial phases, has carried away the lighter materials, leaving behind an accumulation of cassiterite. Under the microscope, two types of cassiterite can be recognised in the stream-tin deposits. One type is angular with the crystal form of the mineral quite well preserved – it looks as if it has not long been liberated from the parent rock source. The other is well-rounded and it has been suggested that this was liberated much earlier, perhaps in the Mesozoic, and was rounded during a period of high sea level, when it was deposited in a beach.

The future – where do we go from here?

So, in our journey through geological time, we have reached the present day; what will happen in the future? We are poised between two unpleasant outcomes; on the one hand we have the threat of global warming and rising sea levels, caused by anthropogenic activity pouring greenhouse gases into the atmosphere. On the other hand, the longer geological perspective suggests that within the next ten thousand years we will return to the 'normal' climate of the last million years, which would be much colder than at present, with perhaps as much as half of the present-day temperate land in the northern hemisphere made uninhabitable by the cold and ice.

We shall be very lucky if we avoid both of these extremes. Remember those frighteningly rapid changes in climate recorded in the Greenland ice cores!

Suggestions for further reading

For those who wish to read more about Cornish geology, the following publications should be obtainable from most bookshops or local-authority libraries:

BIRD, E., 1998. *The Coasts of Cornwall.* Alexander Associates, Fowey. A guide to the coastal scenery of Cornwall by a well-known geomorphologist, with much geological detail.

CAMM, S., 1995, *Gold in the Counties of Cornwall and Devon.* Cornish Hillside Publications, St Austell. An account ot the geology and history of gold production in the two counties.

COLLINS, J.H., 1878. *The Hensbarrow Granite District.* Re-published in facsimile form by Cornish Hillside Publications, 1992. A classic account of the geology of the St Austell granite, and the china-clay industry as it was in the 1870s.

DEARMAN, W.R., FRESHNEY, E.C., KING, A.F., WILLIAMS, M., McKEOWN, M.C., 1970. *Geologists' Association Guide No 10: The North Coast of Cornwall from Bude to Tintagel.* Geologists' Association, Burlington House, London W1V 9AG. A definitive account of the coastal geology; a revised edition is planned.

EDMONDS, E.A., McKEOWN, M.C. and WILLIAMS, M., 1975. *British Regional Geology: South-West England.* British Geological Survey. A useful summary of the geology of South-west England, but getting a little out of date.

EMBREY, P.G. and SYMES, R.F., 1987. *Minerals of Cornwall and Devon.* British Museum (Natural History). A superbly produced book which provides an excellent account of the mineralogy and mining.

FLOYD, P.A., EXLEY, C.S. and STYLES, M.T., 1993. *Geological Conservation Review Series No 5: Igneous Rocks of South-West England.* Chapman and Hall. A detailed and authoritative account of the igneous rocks of Cornwall.

HALL, A., 1994 *Geologists' Association Guide No 19: West Cornwall (2nd Edition).* Geologists' Association, Burlington House, London W1V 9AG. A first-class field guide to the Penwith peninsula, the Lizard, St Agnes and Cligga Head.

HOBSON, D.M., 1978. *Geologists' Association Guide No 38: The Plymouth Area.* Geologists' Association, Burlington House, London W1V 9AG. A useful guide to the Whitsand Bay, Rame Head and Kingsand localities.

ANON (actually MacADAM, J.). *A Geology Guide to North Cornwall.* North Cornwall Coast and Countryside Service, PL31 1LZ. A useful, nicely illustrated guide to the north Cornwall coast, with three geological trails described.

SELWOOD, E.B., DURRANCE, E.M. AND BRISTOW, C.M., 1998. *The Geology of Cornwall and The Isles of Scilly.* University of Exeter Press. This is the natural follow-up to this book; each chapter is written by an expert in the field concerned, providing a great deal of detailed information.

The coverage of British Geological Survey maps and memoirs is given in Chapter 1.

Index

Page numbers in **bold** type indicate the main description of the item

On the Back Cover ...

Kynance Cove from the Rill was painted by **John Clarke Isaac Uren**, born of Cornish parents in Truro in 1845, and died in Penzance in 1932, aged 87. He is buried in Heamoor Cemetery. Uren spent most of his life in the Penzance area, after having gained a free studentship to the Penzance School of Art. He painted mainly marine scenes of the Cornish coast and exhibited at the Royal Academy and the Royal Institute of Water Colours. Although most of his output was in the form of water colours, this painting is an oil.

The painting was described in an art review of an exhibition of Uren's paintings, published in the *Cornish Telegraph* for November 15th, 1883:

"The qualities alluded to are very noticeably present in *Kynance Cove from the Rill*, which is certainly one of the gems from the collection. It is high noon; the tide is low, and the placid sea laps lazily upon the white beach and around the fantastically shaped rocks which are scattered about in such picturesque confusion. Those who have visited this most lovely of the many lovely spots upon our Cornish coast must recognise how difficult it is for an artist to transfer its peculiar charm to canvas, but Mr Uren has been very successful in his attempt. His painting enables one, without having seen the cove itself, to recognise the truth of Swinburne's description of:

> *"The lovely lion guarded strand*
> *Where that huge warder lifts his couchant sides*
> *Asleep, above the sleepless lap of tides,*
> *- - - and past the unsounded caves,*
> *Unscareable, wherein the pulse of waves*
> *Throbs through perpetual darkness, to and fro,*
> *And the blind night swims heavily below."*

The reference to a 'lion' refers to Lion Rock, which can be seen in the top left-hand corner of the painting.

Kynance Cove is composed of bastite and tremolite serpentinite, which represents lower crust/upper mantle material incorporated into the Lizard ophiolite (see **Chapter 5**). One of the most interesting features of the painting is the beach represented in the bottom left-hand corner; for at the present day the position of the beach is occupied by large boulders, and is backed by a large depression known as Lawarnick pit (*Figure 83, page 135*). Although we cannot be sure that the beach is not a product of Uren's artistic license, we get some clue of what may have happened from the 1912 edition of the Geological Survey Memoir (page 239), in which it is reported, in the section on landslips:

"Often the roof of large caves has collapsed and great circular depressions are produced; these are especially common where there are dykes and veins of serpentine. Some of them are more than a hundred yards in diameter and resemble great quarries as they are filled with broken rock, often in enormous pieces. They form one of the characteristic features of the serpentine cliffs and one of the best examples is Lawarnick pit (west of Kynance) ..."

The author is indebted to the Art Curator and Librarian of the Royal Cornwall Museum for much of the above information.